The Fly-Fisher's Plants

Their Value in Trout Waters

D. MACER WRIGHT

Plant and stream drawings by

SUE WHITAKER

DAVID & CHARLES : NEWTON ABBOT

309593

ISBN o 7153 61163

Set in 11 on 13 point Garamond
and printed in Great Britain by
Latimer Trend & Company Ltd
for David & Charles (Holdings) Limited
South Devon House   Newton Abbot   Devon

Contents

5

List of Illustrations

7

Figures 1, 15, 16 and 18–25 are reproduced by courtesy of the Freshwater Biological Association. Figure 17 was drawn by Dr Michael Ladle and the remaining drawings are by Sue Whitaker. All plant figures are approximately one-quarter size

Introduction

THIS STUDY is concerned with the weeds, if so they may be called, of the fly-fisher's waters; their identification, disposition in streams and ponds, the life they carry, their value, and the ways in which they can be used to the benefit of fish and fishermen, or misused to the detriment of both.

Fly fishing means pre-eminently fishing for trout with nymph and dry fly, but it includes wet-fly work and, to a limited extent, the use of nymph and dry fly for coarse fish. The term weeds is unfortunate in the present context, since to most people weeds are rubbish. But in fly fishing the water vegetation plays an indispensable part, because it harbours the nymphs and larvae that make the fishing possible. Without these there would be almost no nymphing or dry-fly angling worth the name, except in swift, rocky streams where nymphs are associated primarily with the mosses and algae of stones, and not with higher plants.

I have devoted a part of this book to aquatic herbicides, materials which I suspect are liable to be applied without sufficient appreciation of the questionable effects they might possibly have, specifically in waters where the dry fly is the predominant or perhaps exclusive method, or where nymph fishing is an accepted technique.

I have necessarily assumed in my readers a fair knowledge of the fundamentals of fly fishing. To have assumed otherwise would have meant lengthy discussions on such things as anglers' flies, their methods of reproduction, life histories and so on, at which rate a book on the fly-fisher's plants would hardly have got started, let alone finished. All I can dare to hope for in the case of those who are not so well informed is that this book will stimulate an increased interest in the various flies, nymphs etc that have flown, crawled and swum in and out of its pages.

CHAPTER 1

The General Picture

THE FLY-FISHER'S plants may best be regarded as those growing in chalk and limestone streams, in streams of lowland pasture outside the chalk and limestone regions, and in trout ponds and small lakes. These by no means cover all trout waters, but they cover most of those in which plants of recognised value appear. Mountain, hill and moorland streams, large lakes and reservoirs, are in different classes. Mountain and hill streams frequently flow down to stony and rocky levels, examples being common in Wales. The stream beds support few of the food-bearing plants of richer waters; instead we find mosses and algae coating the rocks and stones and supporting the nymph stage of anglers' flies. Moorland streams are often too acid for what, in fly-fishing terms, we may regard as high value plants. Such streams do carry certain plants, and may be abundant in trout food, though not always of the kind associated with fly fishing, but the plants cannot often be equated with those of alkaline waters, nor will the variety of invertebrates directly related to fly fishing and harboured by plants in acid streams be as wide as that associated with chalk streams. Such comparative poverty is reflected in the fact that trout in mountain and moorland waters never reach the size of those in chalk streams.

Large lakes and reservoirs may have good weed beds around their margins, but comparatively few further out, and trout will feed largely on forms of water life that are not so dependent on weeds for their existence.

This brings us to the association between weeds and trout food. The living plant itself is of no food value either to the trout or to the animals it supports, and which in turn feed the fish. It is the coating of microscopic organisms, bacteria, algae and protozoa—the 'slime' over the surface of stems and leaves—that provides the food for the nymphs, snails, shrimps, leeches and so on that are eaten by the fish.

This coating is not confined to plants; it appears in various forms on practically every object that finds its way into the water, whether broken branches and twigs, or abandoned bicycles, and it is usually thick on the wooden piles of hatches, bridges and so forth. Its presence everywhere on branches, twigs and suchlike that had fallen into water led the American biologist, W. H. Pond, to suggest in 1905 that plants were merely supports for the microscopic layer, and thirteen years later another biologist, V. E. Shelford, advanced the opinion, presumably in the interests of drainage, that all the larger rooted plants could probably be removed and be replaced by something else of the same form and texture without greatly affecting the conditions of water life.

These theories apparently failed to take into consideration the vital oxygenating role played by aquatic plants, and also pointed to a lack of investigation into plant-animal relationship, where certain species of animals prefer certain species of plants. For example, some *Ephemeroptera* nymphs and the larvae of *Simulium* need high concentrations of oxygen, and will thrive in the main only on plants which provide these.

Some years ago experiments were made in an Anglesey stream, the Afon Ffraw, with plastic weeds designed to simulate *Ranunculus* (water crowfoot). They became colonised not by the species, exceedingly valuable to the fly fisher, that colonise the natural plant, but by creatures making low oxygen demands like certain worms, beetles, shrimps and chironomids, none of which would be of any interest to dry-fly fishers, though a few would be to those using wet flies. But fishing interests apart, the experiment exploded Shelford's theory, for it demonstrated that artificial substitutes for weeds would, indeed, affect the conditions of water life.

In trout streams the disposition of weed beds is fundamental to the variations in flow that are typical of the best waters. In fact, a good keeper looks on his weed beds as essential regulators and diverters of currents. He encourages their growth, or diminishes it, in accordance with the need to slow down the currents in some places and speed them in others. By channelling the flow between beds, he creates fast runnels where necessary to clear out silt, assist the transport of duns and spinners towards the waiting trout and, if needs be, to create bank scours and form pools in which trout will lie. In weedless areas that are poor in fly life and hence unpopulated by trout, he plants appropriate weeds. He cuts where growth is excessive and is holding water and so creating silt, or where it is vital to get the water moving to prevent bank erosion and flooding. Only comparatively rarely does he contemplate complete seasonal removal of top growth, and more rarely still, complete eradication of tops and roots.

He is glad to have controlled bankside growth, not only for its scenic value, but because it offers shelter to fish, camouflage to fishermen, and acts as a bonding agent to give a stable margin to the waterside and to help offset the undermining effects of voles, and the consequent dangers of erosion. He also considers the beauty of such flowering weeds as crowfoot, and recognises that for many anglers much of the charm of fishing lies in the contemplation of massed blossoms on the water, and that not every man with a rod goes to the water with the sole object of catching his limit.

From the foregoing it may perhaps be allowed that my distinction between weeds and plants is valid, and that anyone who regards the term weeds as signifying useless and unwanted growths should revise his opinion as far as aquatic plants are concerned. All species should be conserved in varying degrees, the object being to strike the right balance between the need to regulate growth and the need to preserve the maximum possible fly life. Even the sometimes ubiquitous Canadian pondweed, which can combine ubiquity with iniquity, is valuable in restricted amounts;

it may have to be heavily thinned, but seldom is there a need for its extinction. As we shall see later, this approach has special relevance to certain types of herbicides that remove top growth for an entire season.

It is not always appreciated by those whose prime interest in trout streams is confined to the removal of fish that no stream assumes a permanent inner character, even though it may, superficially, appear to be the same piece of water year after year. It is continually changing. New subsidiary currents appear, remain for a time, then become merged in others; the topography ot the river bed is variable, changing according to local deposits, local erosions, and subsequent transport of deposits as currents are diverted or gain strength. Rivers more subject than those of chalk valleys to flooding and falling levels resulting from rain or drought may show marked changes which, of course, are quite easily perceived. There is continual flux, and chalk stream management in particular involves equally continued attention to plants, removal of silt and so on.

Since this book is concerned with the practical aspects of aquatic plants in everyday fly fishing, we will not make lengthy excursions into complex matters of chemistry and biology. But we must appreciate the fundamental chemical and physical effects which the plants have on the aquatic environment.

In daytime the plants absorb carbon dioxide and produce oxygen, this process being intimately connected with photosynthesis, which is the action of sunlight on the green colouring matter of the leaves, leading to the synthesising into available foods of the nutrient solutions taken in via the roots and translocated to the foliage. Plants therefore aerate the water and provide the oxygen, or a large part of it, which is essential for all fish and aquatic fauna. Some of the latter can exist on low concentrations, but all need oxygen in some degree, and certain species need high concentrations.

At night, when no photosynthesis occurs, carbon dioxide is given off, but usually the amount of oxygen produced during the daylight hours is ample to counteract any heavy and dangerous concentrations of carbon dioxide at night. However, if the plant beds are excessively dense and are associated with much decaying organic matter, then the reduced oxygen and the increased carbon dioxide may cause fish mortality, and will very probably cause mortality among high-oxygen-using fauna in general.

It was mentioned earlier that live aquatic plants do not provide food for the invertebrates that colonise them and feed the trout. There are one or two possible exceptions, though they are probably of little or no significance in fly fishing. A few caddis, stone-fly and chironomid larvae do feed directly on the plant, and a few plant-burrowing species feed similarly, while others burrow into the stems only for shelter.

By far the greatest proportion of plant tissue eaten by aquatic herbivores is dead tissue. This organic detritus is very important to a wide range of creatures which, though in the main of no account in fly fishing, are nevertheless essential members of the water community. Some undoubtedly feed trout, and it is possible that some which feed mainly on the 'slime', or periphyton, of the plants, feed also on the detritus. Two which almost certainly do are snails and shrimps.

For certain types of insects which spend their larval stage in the water and their adult stage in the air, plants provide a connecting link for females depositing eggs and for larvae on the point of emergence as winged adults. The egg-laying females crawl down the stems to lay their eggs, and the emerging larvae crawl up them to reach take-off points as winged forms.

Perhaps one of the most interesting examples of how nature meets the needs of aquatic fauna is found in the provision for oxygen among species that breathe the air of the atmosphere. It is not always realised that the remote ancestry of some aquatic animals was terrestrial. Certain of these have not adapted to a completely submerged existence, using the dissolved oxygen of the water, but must breathe atmospheric air. Thus we find close associations between these insects and the plants that can satisfy their needs. The pondweed *Potamogeton pectinalis* is a case in point; this has large air spaces in its stems, and the stems are punctured by certain larvae in order to tap the air supply.

A fairly high oxygen concentration is essential for trout, and the higher the water temperature, the more the oxygen needed. But the amount of dissolved oxygen falls as the temperature rises, thus the absence of adequate plants may be a limiting factor in the oxygen supply in trout waters during hot weather. This is not always taken into account at weed-cutting times in midsummer. At this period the water temperature may reach about 70° F (20° C), and if this coincides with a fall in oxygen concentration to half saturation, the trout will not be able to absorb more than about 25 per cent of the amount needed for full activity.

Low oxygen and high carbon dioxide lead to a further state dangerous and often fatal to trout. Rainbow are slightly more tolerant than brown trout, but investigations have shown that although the former will survive for at least twenty-four hours when the oxygen concentration is only 20 per cent of saturation, ie two parts per million, and the temperature 62° F (16·5° C) and when no carbon dioxide is present, most will die within one hour if carbon dioxide reaches fifteen parts per million.

A further chemical result of plant decay is the production of ammonia. This is a main waste product of the aquatic environment and is discharged by trout and most aquatic organisms. In healthy rivers it presents no problem, but in rivers highly enriched with nitrogenous substances, of which ammonia is one, the lethal effects of the latter cannot be rapidly neutralised, and since only one part per million is sufficient to reduce the blood oxygen of trout to about 14 per cent of its normal value, it follows that where conditions of excessive ammonia arise, trout will suffer severely.

Only the briefest details of the plant story have here been sketched in but it is hoped that they will be enough to show that, basically, a trout stream depends for its own life, and the life it sustains, on well regulated plant communities. These mean in turn

Page 17 PLATE 1
Source of the River Test: a photograph taken in late August showing the famous 'cup', reduced to low level, with dry watercourse

Page 18 PLATE 2
River Test at Wherwell: a photograph taken on the same day as the one overleaf and showing river at normal summer level

an acceptable level of natural decay, adequate to sustain organisms that feed on detritus, but never so excessive as to cause denitrification and the breakdown of the neutralising and cleansing chemical processes natural to healthy fresh waters.

CHAPTER 2

Chalk Streams

THE CHALK stream is the ideal trout water. Although it is not available to everyone, this must not deter us from examining its plants. It is the yardstick for plant appreciation and management in all trout waters containing higher vegetation. There is also the fact to consider that some streams remote from chalk country possess certain of the chalk stream characteristics. For example, comparative analyses, made by J. M. Hellawell, of the Lugg and the Afon Llynfi, both within the Wye river system of southern central Wales, and of the chalk stream, the Bere, revealed that the first two had a pH of 8·0, and the Bere of 8·3. An earlier study of the Lincolnshire Welland, by J. B. Leeming, showed that the pH of this river was 8·1.

On the basis of their chemical analyses it was plain that the two rivers of the Wye system had much more in common with the chalk stream than most anglers would expect. We sometimes think that because the rich weed beds of chalk streams are so strongly associated with extreme clarity of water, the plants that occur there will inevitably be absent from less clear waters in other regions. This is not always so, as anyone who is familiar with the fine ranunculus beds along the Bodenham stretch of the Herefordshire Lugg will know. This stretch is, in fact, crystal clear at its best, but after floods it becomes heavily charged with particles of red marl, and so is not comparable with chalk streams in this respect.

Such examples could be multiplied many times. There will not usually be the variation in plant species in rivers outside the chalk and limestone regions that occurs within these regions, and frequently there will not be comparable areas of any given species. Nevertheless, valuable plants will certainly be present, and in some rivers the overall plant pattern will not be so very far removed from that of chalk streams, largely because the plants concerned have a wide aquatic habitat, and are not, as they are sometimes thought to be, exclusively related to chalk streams.

Chalk streams, with which we may include streams of limestone country since in fishing terms they are similar, vary in width and depth and rates of flow. The Test, Itchen and Kennet are more accurately called rivers, being wide in many places and having many topographical variations. In some parts they are deep, in others shallow. The Kennet in particular is very fast in some lengths. They all have a main current, but also subsidiary currents caused by the disposition of plants, differences in the river bed, the presence or absence of silt and of gravel.

They receive feeder streams, most of which are narrow and more truly streamlike, and the vegetation of these is usually more limited in species than in the main river. In the latter there are habitats for both slow and fast water plants, whereas in the former, whose flow is more uniformly swift, plants tend to be restricted to those needing a fast flow. Nevertheless, feeders can become little more than ditches if they are neglected, when slow water plants will establish, together with encroaching reeds and rushes. With continued neglect, severe silting, flooding and bank erosion can occur. The feeders will then not only be an embarrassment but will lose their inestimable value as spawning waters for trout, and will harbour the trout's deadliest enemy, namely pike.

The limestone waters, eg those of the Cotswolds, are generally narrower than the main rivers of the chalk country, and so may carry fewer plant varieties, but the best streams, like the Colne, provide magnificent trout fishing. Some have deep and somewhat sluggish lengths, but the best parts of, for example, the Colne, Evenlode and Windrush, compare with anything the chalk valleys can offer, and there are distinct similarities between, say, the Gloucestershire Evenlode and the Berkshire Lambourne, or the Hampshire Dever. Some of the Cotswold streams, such as the Dickler, have a great many twists and turns.

Chalk and limestone waters rise from springs deep in their respective geological formations. Their headwaters are sometimes clearly defined, sometimes not. Those of the Test form a crystal clear pool, described by Harry Plunket Greene in the immortal phrase, 'the cup of water in the meadow at Ashe'; those of the Itchen are an undistinguished and leaf spattered pool half hidden in a small copse at the bend of a lane; those of the Windrush are little more than a seepage from the ground in a farm meadow on the Cotswolds.

But these springs can seldom be identified as the sole source of the rivers, because the headwaters lie in gathering grounds, sometimes of a considerable area whose farthest boundaries are some way from the springs.

Percolation of rain and rising water tables is often a slow process, so that feeding of the main spring is gradual but persistent. Thus chalk streams do not normally become heavily charged at the heads after rain, and so are not subject to violent flooding. Similarly, drought conditions take longer to become evident than in rivers fed directly by rain and hill run-off. The level of the latter may drop severely in drought periods or rise suddenly in wet ones, but although chalk streams do flood after prolonged and heavy rain, or diminish after prolonged drought, both conditions are less sudden and less severe.

When drought conditions arise, the degree to which the chalk stream is affected may depend to a marked extent on the height of the water table at some distance downstream of the spring. For example, the source of the Test often diminishes in summer to the point where the 'cup' becomes a mere spoonful; the margins of the pool and the water-course leading from it will be quite dry, and the impression can be gained that the river must have dwindled in consequence (Plate 1, p 17). Yet a fairly short walk along the course will bring us to the first signs of water, and before long we shall find the stream flowing strongly (Plate 2, p 18).

The ground in which the spring lies is high in relation to the river valley; thus although the spring water cannot in drought periods reach the surface abundantly enough to fill the watercourse and supply the river, the river is nevertheless supplied at the lower ground level from the water table, which does reach the river floor in adequate amounts. Here we have a clear illustration of the fact that although the spring or wellhead is the geographical source, the river is not entirely dependent on this for its existence.

Such a feature does not, of course apply, universally, especially where the small stream, or 'winterbourne' is concerned. Many of these dry out completely in midsummer, when it is possible to walk along their entire length over grass and weeds.

The speed of chalk streams, particularly of wide ones like the Test and Itchen, is often greater than it appears to be, and the main current often deceptively strong. But it is very difficult to arrive at average river speeds, because the flow can vary greatly from place to place, depending on water depth, the distance from the bank and from weed beds at which measurements are made, and the effects of subsidiary currents.

However, in general terms, chalk streams would come into the category classified by A. G. Tansley as Zone 3. Rivers in this zone have relatively moderate currents of about 1–2ft (0·30–0·60m) per second; the beds are of light shingle and gravel, non-silted in parts and lightly silted elsewhere (though often heavily silted when neglected) (Plate 3, p 35). They are highly calcareous; a figure of 92 parts per million of calcium for the Itchen has been quoted by R. W. Butcher. They support a long catalogue of plants, among which are species so indispensable to dry-fly fishing that without them this method of angling would not be possible.

A notable feature of the Itchen, and one which is shared by the Test to the same extent, and probably in varying degrees by most strong current waters in or out of the chalk valleys, is that there are frequent additions in plant locations. Pieces of plants are broken off the parent beds and carried away until they meet some obstruction in the shallows, when they root and become the nucleus of new beds. This movement contributes, sometimes significantly, to continual changes in the topography of the river bed, in the speed of flow and direction of currents, and in the disposition of fauna which inhabit the particular plant.

In some measure it is nature's way of keeping the water alive, and it goes some way towards ensuring the variations in the stream pattern that fly fishermen appreciate. It can also have undesirable effects, if beds become established in parts of the river where their presence arrests the flow and causes silting up, as in the picture on p 35. This can certainly happen with Canadian pondweed which, even in the aristocratic chalk streams, is by no means unknown. This plant spreads by fragmentation, and pieces carried down by the current can easily root and give rise to dense growths that can not only cause silting up, but can also choke out valuable plants like crowfoot. It is possible for the latter to be so weakened in the presence of enveloping pondweed that an affected bed may die within three years, or even less.

But of course plant fragmentation can also help, though often to a limited extent, to prevent existing beds from building up to excessive proportions.

This more or less continual change in the densities of plant beds, sometimes appreciable, sometimes only slight, has led some people to doubt whether there is much point in planting new beds. The argument is that nature evens things out and may nullify the effects of special planting. This is probably true as a basic principle, and since it is difficult to make long-term evaluations of planting, because of the continual changes that are taking place, the argument has validity. But the point is that chalk-stream improvements are also basically short lived and must therefore be undertaken regularly, year in, year out. There is no once for all measure, and a man does not plant a new bed and then forget it. Neither does he lose heart if the results are not exactly as he had expected. And if they are the opposite of what he hoped for, and the planting proves to have been a mistake, he will have learnt a most useful lesson.

I have known stretches of side streams that were rather feature-less and devoid of good trout lies to have been vastly improved in the short term directly through planting crowfoot. The new beds caused divisions in the current that animated hitherto sluggish water and cleared away silt, and replaced useless marginal areas by pools in which trout took up residence. Also the beds brought fly life where previously this had been scarce.

In some instances the beds were wrongly sited, and they then caused silt to deposit immediately above them. This occurred where they were planted in mid-stream right in the path of the main current. Stream planting is something like planting a wind-break; the latter should filter the wind, never block it; true, you plant in the path of the wind, but with the trees so arranged that they never present a solid barrier, but instead absorb and filter the wind. Stream planting should filter and deflect the current, not block it. In time, the water will tend to glide round the edges of the bed, if upstream silt is allowed to establish, and the filtering effect will diminish. This can appreciably alter the disposition of the plant fauna, and sometimes cause a definite change in the species inhabiting the plant, a subject that will be discussed later.

Here we have an example of how conditions change, whether as a result of plant management, or its lack, or as a result of con-tinual flexibility in the river pattern. Moderate silting of plant beds is not necessarily an evil; it happens anyway, no matter how we may try to avoid it, and as it creates a micro-habitat within the plant that is favoured and sought by certain aquatic animals on which trout feed, it is obviously not only to the angler's advantage, but is also a dispensation of nature. Excessive silt is of course a different matter, and to be prevented.

When we talk about the constantly changing stream pattern—and this involves not only plants, but also things less tangible to the ordinary fisherman, like chemistry, oxygen values, tempera-tures and so on, which may fluctuate appreciably throughout the length of a river—we may fall into the error of imagining that God's in his heaven, all's right with the watery world; in other words that nature will see that everything in the river is taken care of and that she will strike a balance acceptable to fishermen. To imagine that would be to shuffle off on to the Almighty a responsibility which He will not accept. The good Lord, in his infinite wisdom, has little use for those who will not help themselves. If we neglect chalk streams, which are among the true heavenly gifts bestowed upon mankind, then the plants will assume an altogether different character and will become enemies instead of allies, choking out the trout and ruining the water.

This is because chalk streams are very rich in nutrient salts and so promote strong growth of a wide range of plants, a condition that is encouraged by their comparative freedom from floods, and so from large-scale disintegration and carrying away of plants. It is a sorry state of affairs when a beautiful plant like water crowfoot spreads across a stream to cause bank flooding and to make fishing impossible. To the uninformed it may present a pretty picture, and on the banks of the Dever, at a spot where the stream was choked by this plant, I heard a literary-looking gentleman ecstatically quoting the Dorset poet, William Barnes,

O small-fëaced flow'r that now dost bloom
To stud wi' white the shallor Frome,

The quotation was apt, even if the location was wrong, though it transpired that the literary gent had no idea what the flower was, nor for that matter, the name of the stream. I remembered the American lady who startled my son when he was fishing the Itchen one day, by 'prezooming' the river was the Thames.

As far as chalk-stream vegetation is concerned, we may fairly sum up by saying that rarely, if ever, will there be a dearth of plants, but in the absence of plant management there may well be a superabundance. In most streams and rivers of the chalk and limestone valleys the balance between the optimum and the excessive is nearly always delicate, if not in any one season, then certainly over several seasons as a whole. This is generally recognised by all whose fishing is done in these waters, and it is also generally recognised that if plants are left to themselves the balance will almost inevitably become tilted to the excessive. What is not so generally recognised is that, rich as these streams are in vegetation, the wrong management can turn the balance the other way, when instead of there being optimum plant growth, there will be a shortage. This is a ticklish subject, to be debated in due course.

One other type of chalk stream deserves mention, namely the small brook or bourne. Several of these flow over a more or less semi-permeable valley floor that is overlaid with gravel. In dry seasons the water table often sinks below the valley floor and the springs are inadequate to boost it up. When this happens the streams disappear and all that is left is dry vegetation. If the streams contain trout, and unhappily wild specimens do find their way into them, there can be high mortality. Such brooks would not, of course, be stocked with stew-raised trout.

CHAPTER 3

Other Streams

I HAVE already classed trout streams outside the chalk and limestone regions as those of lowland pasture, as far as food-bearing
plants are concerned and as far as they apply specifically to fishing
with nymph and dry fly. The classification is somewhat arbitrary,
for two reasons. First, there are streams within the category that
can be found in areas other than lowland pasture, and second,
many waters of the type are not true trout streams, but have been
taken over by fly-fishing clubs and have had trout introduced.
However, lowland pasture may, I think, be accepted as a fair
designation of the country where the majority of the waters occur,
and even if they are not trout streams by nature, they may be
considered suitable if they provide reasonable fishing.

Their classification according to Tansley's system is not clear
cut; they possess many of the characteristics of Zones 3 and 4, and
some of Zone 5. The last two are respectively medium to slow,
and very slow or negligible, though the properties of Zone 5 are
not dominant, but local. If they were dominant the streams would
not be suitable for trout.

The river beds vary between sand, silt and mud, gravel and
stones, and the speed of flow from 3ft (0·91m) or even more, per
second at flood to 5in (0·12m) per second at the slowest. The
zonal classification of these rivers is made more difficult by the
fact that the headwaters of some are in the habitat termed torrential, and which belongs to Zone 1, shading off into Zone 2. But
few, and probably none, would come into this class in general
terms, since in the absence of flood conditions their speed is
seldom more than moderate.

In fact we are up against a dilemma in trying to place rivers neatly into zones, at least as far as plants and aquatic fauna are concerned, firstly because the variations in any given stream or river mean that local areas may be totally different from the character of the river in the broadest sense, and secondly because plants and animals are closely related to local variations rather than to the river as a whole. In the first instance we may have almost torrential conditions at the base of a weir or a waterfall, as depicted in Plate 4, p 36, or immediately downstream of a hatchway as in Plate 5, p 36, while immediately above the water may be quite gentle. Shortly below the turbulence it will start to lose speed, so that twenty or thirty yards downstream the flow may be faster than that just above the weir, but slower than where the water comes over. Thus we shall have within a distance of perhaps forty yards three different rates of flow, and in each area a particular plant-animal habitat may evolve. Or there may be no such habitat in the torrential or semi-torrential zone, and trout may simply lie at the edge of this or in the 'vacuum' beneath the turbulence, waiting for food to be washed over the weir.

Tansley's system is really more appropriate to water engineering, for which it was primarily devised, than to freshwater biology, and several workers, British and continental, have made different approaches in the latter field, basing their categories on the species of fish inhabiting the different types of water. In 1928 Dr Kathleen Carpenter divided British rivers into four main zones, Headstreams and Highland Brooks, Troutbecks, the Minnow Reach, and the Lowland Reach. The last two are still somewhat general classifications, but are perhaps as near as one can get in fishing terms.

Relating them to Tansley, we can say that Headstreams and Highland Brooks are usually torrential, though not invariably; Troutbecks nearly always are; these two classes therefore occupy Tansley's Zones 1 and 2, and do not concern our present study, since they are virtually devoid of higher plants. The Minnow Reach and the Lowland Reach would correspond approximately with Tansley's Zones 3 and 4 respectively, but with the Lowland having certain characteristics of his Zone 5.

The Lowland Reach is definitely coarse-fish water, slow, meandering, with mainly a mud bed and much slow-water vegetation. On the continent it is called the bream reach, which speaks for itself.

Dr Carpenter's Minnow Reach is the one that principally merits our consideration. Continental workers call this the grayling zone, which fits a number of English trout streams of lowland pasture, though the term was unacceptable to Dr Carpenter on the grounds that grayling are not sufficiently widespread in Britain to warrant the classification.

We must distinguish coarse fish in rather specific terms in relation to the Minnow Reach and the Lowland Reach. Although the former carries coarse fish, these are likely to be confined to those few species that are at home in trout waters, together with one or two that inhabit the slower parts of a trout stream, like roach and perch. Often the territories of these are well defined, and do not include those of trout. The Lowland Reach, in contrast, will carry few or no dace, and no grayling, but it will have the various species that come under the general heading of coarse fish. Pike, of course, are almost everywhere, Minnow Reach or not.

The great virtue of Dr Carpenter's system of zoning is that it recognises that any given river usually contains fish territories appropriate to fish species. Thus her Minnow Reach would carry not only minnows, but possibly trout and grayling, trout and dace, or any of these species on its own, though it is more probable that at least two of them, either trout and grayling, or trout and dace, will share the territory, if share is the right word. Where these different fish do occupy the same water, their mutual attitude is more likely to be one of unremitting competition, even open warfare, than of amicable co-existence.

They occupy the same habitat when it suits them equally, and they feed on similar organisms. This does not mean that a trout habitat necessarily implies suitability for dace or grayling; the former will frequently be found in streams that are deep enough for trout but not for grayling, and it is perhaps rather exceptional to find all three in the same territory. What we do find—and the larger chalk streams of Hampshire provide perfect examples—is territory shared, or disputed by trout and grayling, while in streams of the Minnow Reach category in pastoral lowland we find dace together with trout. But in the latter instance the water is sometimes not 'natural' trout water, and contains no wild trout, but only the stew-raised stock introduced by a fishing club.

It is not uncommonly an unfortunate feature of streams that do not carry wild trout, but into which raised specimens have been introduced, that they cannot support trout and dace sufficiently to enable the former to reach anything like the size of their chalk-stream brethren. One possible reason is that there are not enough food-bearing plants to sustain an adequate diet for two types of fish which both feed to a considerable extent on the same organisms.

It should be mentioned, while we are on the subject of the Minnow Reach, that logically this category includes stretches of many chalk streams, and in those stretches will be found the chief coarse fish of chalk waters, namely grayling, and pike will soon become established in the deeper and slower reaches of chalk streams if they are given the chance.

Where the Minnow Reach waters of lowland pastures differ distinctly from chalk streams, quite apart from the differences that can occur in the relative calcium contents, is that the latter flow over a geological formation that is basically the same throughout most of the river length, whereas the lowland pasture streams outside the chalk regions may flow over several different formations.

This can be reflected in the type of vegetation. As was intimated earlier, the plants of the two types of water are often similar, but whereas there is generally an abundance of all plants common to chalk rivers in these rivers, with perhaps half-a-dozen distinct species growing strongly within an area of 100 square yards, in the other type of water those half-dozen species may form only comparatively small beds, and may be separated by appreciable lengths of water. It is not only the disparate geological formations that are involved; indeed these are unlikely to be in such short lengths along a river bed as to determine immediately defined plant locations, except sometimes where rocky or stony stretches intervene between those of mud or silt, but there can be little doubt that there is an association between the substratum and the plants it supports, just as there is between a soil and its plants.

This brings us to what may be regarded as a key plant indicator for fly-fishing waters, namely water crowfoot. We shall deal in detail with our plants in due course, but here it is pertinent to mention that wherever the fast-water species of the genus *Ranunculus* are found we can feel that fly-fishing possibilities are present, since these species harbour major items of trout food and also occupy the type of water that trout prefer.

Crowfoot is one of the first primary fly-fishing plants to appear in the Minnow Reach. It will not grow in the most rapid zones higher upstream, but it begins to take root where the initial water speed has slackened off to the moderately fast flow of the middle and lower middle stretches. It gives us an excellent idea of the different speeds between headwaters of chalk streams and headwaters of streams fed by rain and hill run-off. In the former we shall often find at least one species of crowfoot right up in the headwaters, indicating a moderately fast flow, but not a torrent, from the springs. In the headwaters of rain-fed rivers we shall seldom find the plant, and it will normally start to appear only at places at some appreciable distance from the river's source. The longer the length of the Minnow Reach, the greater the amount of crowfoot, and hence the longer the fly-fishing stretch. As the Minnow Reach merges into the Lowland, water crowfoot will become less evident, and if it appears at all in the coarse-fish territory it will be largely confined to a few slow-water species not associated with trout.

Again we have a distinct difference between plant locations in chalk and in hill-fed streams. In the former, crowfoot of some species or other will be found throughout virtually the whole length of the river, owing to the more or less common geology of the bed and the common speed of the main current. In the other type of water, where these factors are more variable, we often find concentrations of crowfoot interspersed with lengths of water where the plant is absent, or where the fast-water species typical of trout streams are replaced by slow-water species.

This is a further reflection of water speeds. Many streams of the pastoral lowlands outside chalk areas assume different characteristics, even within the length of the Minnow Reach. In some places they flow twice or even three times as fast as in other places; immediately downstream of bends and necks the water gathers speed; along straight stretches it is slower; in areas formed by generations of bank scouring there may be pools almost the size of small ponds. To discover the correlations between these conditions and the various plants demands a strong devotion to the subject, but where the study is undertaken it will be found that such correlations exist and that in some areas plants occupy sufficient space, and that enough species appear, to form a macro habitat, while in other places the area occupied and the species involved will be so small as to constitute nothing larger than a micro habitat.

Southern England, outside the chalk country, including the Midlands, comprises the main region of our lowland pasture streams. Further north we come to the limestone rivers of Yorkshire and the rocky troutbecks of the fells; in the south-west we are in the region of moorland streams; west of the Usk and the Monnow are the rapid, rocky and boulder hill streams of Wales, though some streams, particularly of mid-Wales, are pastoral in character and contain excellent beds of crowfoot.

Although we are not concerned with rocky and stony waters in our context of higher plants, we will touch briefly on their fly-fishing value, if only to correct any notion that because they are not included in this book they are being automatically dismissed as of no account.

They are known as streams of unstable or eroding substrata, ie those whose stony and pebbly beds are subjected to regular movement by the current. Rolling stones, we are told, gather no moss, and if we examine the pebbles of stony streams we shall find that a great many are perfectly clean, like seashore shingle. But we shall also find that there are larger stones or boulders embedded in the surface of the river bottom, as well as rocky outcrops, ledges and so on (Plate 6, p 53). These will have a coating of mosses and algae, and among this coating we shall find innumerable nymphs of anglers' flies, a common one being *Ecdyonurus torrentis*, which has no popular name, but whose specific name is very descriptive. This species may be considered a cousin of the Late March Brown, *E. venosus* (Fig 1). Another nymph we shall find is the Large Dark Olive, *Baëtis rhodani*.

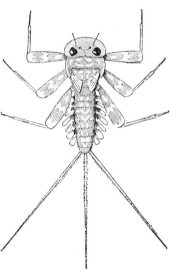

These nymphs are high oxygen users, and in waters carrying higher plants much of the oxygen needed is supplied by the plants. In stony, plantless waters it is supplied by the continual, swift movement of the water, an aerating process so efficient that some waters of this type produce proportionally as many nymphs, at least of Large Dark Olive, as do chalk streams, and in some seasons may produce more. They do not have the same variety of species as are found in streams containing higher plants, because

FIG 1　Nymph of Late March Brown, *Ecdyonurus venosus*, 11mm long, from life

the species are generally limited to the streamlined and the flattened types that offer least resistance to the current and so can

Page 35 PLATE 3 Limestone trout stream heavily silted, with somewhat deeper pool in foreground

Page 36   PLATE 4   (*above*) Semi-torrential conditions downstream of a 'boom', or man-made waterfall; PLATE 5 (*below*) similar conditions below a hatchway

cling to stones while the water washes over their bodies. In the case of the *Baëtis* nymphs, we perceive one of the many ways in which nature adapts to meet particular conditions. Their gills are less developed than are those of nymphs whose primary habitat is slower water, and the gills do not move to activate the surrounding water and thus aerate it. The fact that the nymphs can absorb sufficient oxygen without the need to create oxygenating conditions, illustrates the aerating properties of the streams.

Other high oxygen users whose presence in stony streams is an indication of the aerating properties of the water are certain species of *Simulium* larvae which spin a net over smooth stones. This acts as an anchorage, and together with the 'suction pads' possessed by the larvae, ensures a firm hold against the swift water. Two such species are *S. monticola* and *S. variegatum*. Generally, these are not found as plant clingers in slower, but still relatively rapid rivers, which shows how definite specific differences occur within the genus.

Another interesting example of adaptation is found in the nymphs of the March Brown, *Rithrogena harrupi*, which occur on stones in fast waters, usually in the river rather than the stream category, the Usk being a typical March Brown river. These nymphs have large gill plates so arranged that they create a suction effect, enabling the nymph to cling with great firmness to smooth stones. It is easy to appreciate how efficient this mechanism is by holding under a vigorous waterfall a stone to which the nymphs are attached, when it will be observed that they remain securely anchored.

In the case of *Ecdyonurus* species the adaptation to fast water takes the form of a flattened body—a feature also of March Brown—which offers the least resistance to the current.

We must now leave the stone clingers to their own affairs, and take a look at our final type of water, which is the still water of trout ponds and small lakes.

c

CHAPTER 4

Still Waters

I DO NOT know the size at which a trout pond becomes a small lake. In my fishing district our main still water covers about three acres, and is called a pond. Lake sounds better in angling brochures, but those not concerned with status symbols would probably consider that a still-water trout fishery does not warrant the grander title unless it reaches four acres. However that may be, it is the smaller water that will contain the most rooted plants of value to fly fishers. That is why trout rise to flies comparatively rarely on large waters, and instead feed on fish fry and the various creatures that are represented by underwater artificials. The term 'still waters' is of course one of convenience; few trout ponds and lakes are without a feeder of some kind, and an outlet.

Plants cannot exist without light, for without light photosynthesis is impossible, and without that the complicated processes of food manufacture for plant growth is equally impossible. Light does not penetrate far into water, particularly where there is much sedimentary matter in suspension, thus in large, deep areas of water plants will be confined to the upper layer, ie the epilimnion. The depth of this that is colonised by plants will depend on the angle at which the shoreline shelves down to deep water, first to the thermocline, the layer immediately below the epilimnion, and finally to the deepest zone, the hypolimnion.

If there is a very gentle shelving for a considerable distance, then all the water above the shelf will be a plant habitat, but many lakes either have a gently sloping shoreline that is only marginal in width, and then descends rapidly to deep water, or else there is a steep decline close off shore, leading to deep water a few yards from the shoreline.

The trout pond, ie our 3-4 acre water—or it may be less, for trout will live happily in half an acre ot water if it is spring fed— is seldom deeper than 10-15ft (3-4½m). The hypolimnion, if there is one, will be correspondingly shallower, and will occupy a relatively small part of the pond, since the pond bed will usually be the base of a fairly gently shelving basin. Thus quite an appreciable area extending out from the shoreline, and including this, will be suitable for plants.

The distinct division, in limnology, of water layers that exists in lakes may hardly obtain in ponds, and only an epilimnion may exist, or if lower layers are present, they may be so defined merely by virtue of their lower temperatures, rather than by the depths at which they occur, and the depth which the coldest layer occupies.

The virtual lack of a hypolimnion in ponds is one factor in their 'richer' nature when compared with most large lakes. In the latter, much 'energy material' in the form of decaying matter that is broken down by fungi and bacteria for the use of other organisms falls to the hypolimnion. Here it is still subject to decay, but the oxygen used during this process becomes a diminishing factor, and may finally vanish. If the biological cycle of what we may call birth through death is to proceed, the compounds resulting from bacterial action on the fallen debris must rise to the surface layers to become subjected to the life-building influences present in these, like heat, oxygen and sunlight. But they can reach the surface only when the seasonal conditions of autumn, principally the effects of strong winds, cause the two layers of water to mix, and by then it is too late for significant biological activity.

During winter many substances that might, in different circumstances, have been utilised in the life cycle of the lake inhabitants will be washed away through the lake outlets, and so their full potential will never be realised.

A factor that inhibits marginal areas of plant growth round large lakes, but is much less evident in ponds, is wave action. Anglers familiar with the Welsh lakes will know how rocky and plantless many of the shores of these are. Wave action is frequently very vigorous, and the water beats against the shoreline, making a perhaps scarcely discernible impact on the rocks, but washing away the deposits among them. This has, of course, been going on for thousands of years, except in the case of man-made lakes, and whatever drift or other type of formation once overlay the rocks has disappeared long ago.

The wave-washed deposits are carried away to deeper areas, where they are of no use to higher plants, or away from the lake altogether via the exit stream, or else to sheltered bays. In the latter instance they form suitable plant habitats, though the plants that establish are often tall emergents not greatly used by the animals on which trout feed. Nevertheless, the water around the edges of these plant habitats is often colonised by pondweed, stonewort and other submerged plants, and is favoured by trout, because it is calmer and out of the main wave-washed regions. These sheltered bays are about the only places where a dry fly stands much chance when the main area of water is strongly agitated.

Ponds, being smaller and often sheltered by trees, do not suffer wave action to anything like the same extent. The surface is seldom completely calm all over for any protracted period; a breeze across the pond will ruffle the water, and there is nearly always some kind of commotion going on at intervals throughout the day among coots and moorhens, which helps to keep the surface disturbed. But even the autumn gales do not create the type of extremely choppy water that occurs in lakes.

Perhaps the governing factor in the growth of rooted plants in ponds (rooted as distinct from the floating, rootless species) is the depth to which sunlight penetrates. If the water is cloudy with suspended particles, or dense with organisms, then even quite shallow areas may be without rooted vegetation. On the other hand, areas 6ft deep and more under clear water will sustain good plant growth, especially of Canadian pondweed.

One of the less acceptable aspects of trout ponds is the amount of algae, often called flannel weed, that rises to the surface in hot weather. There are some 2,000 species of green algae, and although they belong to the least evolved members of the plant kingdom, they are, as it were, part of the base or foundation of the great pyramid of living creatures the apex of which is man. They have been described as primary producers of living material. Algal growths massed on the pond surface are an undoubted curse when it comes to fly casting (Plate 7, p 54), but their presence does indicate a rich environment. And although they are such a nuisance in the season when they occur, they can provide a bonus for the following year if the more abundant food they represent enables larger numbers of larvae to survive the winter and to reach the spring in a flourishing state.

Though primitive, these plant forms can utilise solar energy for the synthesising of carbohydrates from water and carbon dioxide, while aquatic animals cannot and must rely for their sustenance on algal and other plant forms, whether living algae or decaying remains of higher plants, and on other nutritional and body-building organisms. In the presence of certain nutritional elements in the water, algae can form proteins as well.

Thus we have the start of the food chain, the further links of which are the animals that feed on the algae, the trout that feed on the animals, and the man who feeds on the trout. This is an extremely simplified description of an exceedingly complex process, about which a lot still remains to be learnt.

It is necessary to distinguish richness in still waters that is of the right kind, and richness of the wrong kind. In the latter case the term is somewhat paradoxical, because it really denotes some degree of pollution, like an over-full stomach that revolts to produce indigestion. It occurs when the water of the hypolimnion is supercharged with nutrient salts, a condition leading to denitrification and lack of oxygen. The process may be natural, especially where the water is calcareous, since calcium plays a major part in decomposition, or it may be much aggravated by run-off of agricultural residues which find their way into the water. Generally, it is accompanied by increased algal growths, not always of a desirable kind, and in any case to an extent that makes further demands on the already limited oxygen, besides making fishing a most frustrating business and living conditions for fish extremely precarious.

Ponds are obviously more at risk than large areas of water, since the latter possess greater reserves of oxygen in their epilimnion, and as there is little or no plant life there, there are fewer oxygen-using and carbon-dioxide-producing organisms. In fact the condition does not arise in large lakes until all the oxygen in the hypolimnion has been used, and this does not happen unless there is a strong and large body of oxygen users in the top layer of water.

In ponds, where there is virtually no hypolimnion, and where the water temperature is higher, and oxygen use is more constant throughout the entire water depth, de-nitrification proceeds more quickly and more uniformly. However, when it is a purely natural phenomenon, nature generally manages to cope with the situation, but when it is a man-made state, then the word pollution is appropriate. It is probably true to say that lakes seldom reach a stage of gross pollution except at the hands of man, and there are scores of examples around the world. The same thing goes generally for ponds, except that small ones may be fouled by cattle or even by ducks, to the point at which life in them becomes almost extinct, save for organisms that are associated with animal detritus, and a few pollution-tolerant creatures like bloodworms.

Richness above a certain limit is undesirable in trout ponds, but provided it is a natural process we cannot do a great deal about it, and must accept it, knowing that nature will put things right fairly soon, by a good rainstorm and a drop in temperature. Some people start hurling hundredweights of lime into the water, or rather tipping it in, often without any very clear idea of what they are trying to achieve.

Lime is undoubtedly good when the water is acid, but acidity is a different thing altogether from the richness we are talking about. To give them their technical terms, waters excessively rich in nutrient salts and suffering high degrees of de-nitrification are known as eutrophic waters; those that are acid are known as dystrophic, and contain, not polluting or de-nitrifying agents, but deposits of organic matter which lie more or less inert on the pond bed, because there is no calcium in the water to effect decomposition. The deposits are thus associated not with an abundance of nutrient salts, but with a scarcity, and in these circumstances plants of value to trout fishing cannot grow.

In short, eutrophic waters are gorged; dystrophic waters are starved.

If we put lime into eutrophic waters we are in danger of making matters worse, because the calcium already present is one of the primary agents in the excessive decomposition. If we put it into dystrophic waters we stand a good chance of starting the essential biological processes of decomposition and of maintaining them at a desirable rate, if we continue liming the pond long enough.

The two conditions not only differ fundamentally, but also in duration. Assuming eutrophy to be not man-made but simply a seasonal feature, it will not as a rule become permanent, but will be adjusted by the cleansing processes of nature. Dystrophy, on the other hand, is more likely to remain a feature of the pond unless man and his bags of lime (often magnesian limestone for preference) intervene.

I said earlier that chalk streams are rich in nutrient salts, and having now implied that in ponds such richness can be associated with undesirable consequences, I may be accused of confusion of thought. We will therefore diverge a moment to consider this apparent anomaly.

The richness of chalk streams would soon lead to de-nitrification with all its manifold ills if it were not for the cleansing effect of the main current. A chalk stream lives by its current; remove that, by bore-hole abstraction from the springs, and the stream will die. Or allow weeds to become so excessive that they seriously impede the current, then the stream will be only half alive, not to mention the bank erosion which the flooding will cause.

Bore-hole abstraction has already killed most of the chalk streams of Hertfordshire within my lifetime, and I have not yet 'fall'n into the sere, the yellow leaf'. The results of abstraction, at least when it removes large quantities of water and severely diminishes the volume and strength of the current, prove beyond all reasonable doubt that the extreme richness of chalk streams soon becomes pollution when the current is cut off. This danger is much greater today than it was in the early days of moderate extraction, because then there were not the many extraneous and potentially lethal substances finding their way into rivers that there are today. There were not the sewage effluents, whether efficiently or inefficiently treated, from large-scale housing development; there were not the innumerable detergents, industrial wastes, agricultural residues and road washings that are now poured and flung into our rivers, or reach them via land drainage.

All this impedimenta contributes, or can contribute, to the chemical degeneration of fresh waters. When it gets into rivers that are by nature so rich in nutrient salts that the balance between purity and impurity is a delicate one, only to be maintained by unremitting attention to weed beds in order to keep the current moving freely, then any severe diminution of the current is certain to cause disaster.

This question of abstraction and man-made pollution is a further divergence, but I have touched on it in an effort to point out that although chalk streams possess the potential for natural de-nitrification, probably to a degree higher than any other type of water, they seldom fail to cope adequately with the problem when man and nature work together so that weeds are efficiently managed and the streams kept moving. In other words, as with lakes, so with chalk streams; pollution in its accepted sense of being a chemically derived condition is caused not by nature, but by man.

It could be useful to draw a mental sketch of a trout pond. In doing so we might be accused by pedants of trying to typify something that refuses to conform to type, on the grounds that a

typical trout pond does not exist. They would have a point, because in the larger context no ponds are exactly similar, any
more than rivers are. However, we must have a starting point, or
we shall never move at all, and all trout ponds possess some
common features.

Let us imagine an irregularly shaped pool fed by a small stream
and set among woodland with waterside alders, its pH roughly
neutral during summer and somewhat lower in winter. Depth
would vary from about 1ft (30cm) at the margins to about 12ft
(3·6m) in the deepest parts. Maximum summer temperature at 6ft
would average about 60° F (16° C) while at the margins it may
reach 70° F (21° C).

The margins out to 3ft or so would be mud overlaid with
leaves where there were bankside alders, but where these were
absent there might be dense growths of celery. This 3ft-wide band
would give way to one 4-6ft deep and approximately 6ft wide,
though with many variations, with 6ft holes of greatly differing
areas. In these Canadian pondweed could be the predominant
plant, but there would also be clumps of water lilies, possibly
white and yellow.

Also within the 6ft depth, and especially where there were bays,
we might see profuse growths of Spiked Water Milfoil, and perhaps
of the delicately flowered Water Violet. If there were large areas of
Broad-leaved Pondweed, these would be approximately 6ft deep,
and it is quite possible that this plant would be the dominant one
throughout areas of that depth.

In addition to these plants there might be scattered communities
of marginal species like Bogbean, Rush, Burr-reed, Shore-weed
and of such plant-like algae as the Stoneworts. The remainder of
the pond would be the 12ft deep centre, but again there could be
many local depth variations within this area.

The plant-animal relationship of our fishing waters are the
subject of a separate chapter, so I will not confuse matters by
dealing with them here, but it is worth taking a look at this point
at the emergence times of a few of the anglers' flies, because so

often the view is expressed that trout ponds are dead until the evening rise, and that evening is the only worthwhile fishing time. In fact this does apply to some ponds, but the lack of insect and fish activity in the earlier hours of the day is not as universal as it is sometimes thought to be.

From beds of Spiked Water Milfoil there could be good hatches of at least one chironomid species about noon in the early part of the season. The shallow areas populated by celery could harbour Lake Olives that might emerge about midday in May. By midsummer there could be perceptible midday activity from Lake and Pond Olives, though the former would be less in hot weather and would be less in any case in ponds than in lakes. From the same area we should see Claret Duns.

The marginal areas of mud and leaves could yield good hatches of chironomids in June during midmorning. Generally, some emergence from midmorning to about 2pm would often be found throughout summer, though the pattern might be very varied as regards species.

The main emergence periods from early to late summer would be the evening, often reaching its peak just after sunset with strong hatches of chironomids and caenis. The former exhibit a strong response to approaching dusk and some of the best trout are caught on pupal representations at this time. Noon emergence of chironomids would decrease markedly after about mid-May and would be replaced by the sunset phase.

The season's activity would start in strength when the water out to 5 or 6ft from the banks was about 48° F (9° C) and when day length was about thirteen hours.

So often the habit is followed in still waters of casting more in hope than on the basis of selection. We get much closer to the true angling spirit if we select spots that we know from personal observation contain plant beds that yield concentrations of insects on which the trout will feed. We get even closer if we relate the plant to the insect, and the insect to its emergence time, so that instead of simply thrashing away with fancy patterns, we select from the fly box those patterns that represent the creatures the trout are taking. Also we shall be more likely to catch fish.

This brings us to the end of our consideration of the main types of water. Our survey has been brief, or at least that is how I hope it will appear, for I should hate it to seem long-winded. Whichever it is, it has left out multitudes of facts, figures and hypotheses. Nevertheless, I hope it has embraced enough to serve the overall purpose it set out to serve. Let us now turn to descriptions of the plants.

CHAPTER 5

The Main Plants

PLANT DESCRIPTIONS for non-botanical works are notoriously difficult because of the need to compromise between technical and popular terms. Where there is no risk of confusion it is probably best to use everyday language. Once we embark on technical terms we become bogged down in 'translations', or we have to resort to a glossary.

This is a book for anglers, the great majority of whom seek to identify a water plant by its leaves. Only where detailed study is concerned are fishermen interested in the plant as a whole—its roots, leaves, flowers and fruit, and there are several scientific books of the highest excellence which will satisfy the needs of the amateur botanist.

My aim has therefore been to concentrate on those parts of the plant most easily accessible and most easily seen. Where the flowers are an obvious aid to identification I have included brief, non-technical descriptions, but fruits have been mainly excluded. These are not usually essential for the present purpose, and in any case full description is virtually impossible without using many technical terms.

I have used British measures, except for very small lengths, which are given in millimetres, these being easier to reckon than fractions of inches. All measurements are averages, as they must be to accommodate the variations that occur in nature. Flowering times are similarly based on averages. The appearance of the first flowers of any given plant may be several days later in midland or northerly areas than in southerly, perhaps as many as fourteen, and duration of flowering periods may vary in the same way.

My grouping does not follow conventional divisions, because I am concerned with the importance of plants in fly fishing, and I have thought it better to group the most important ones first, and to deal with the less important later, even though this does mean that the arrangement is not systematic in the botanical sense. The plants are not, however, given in any order of importance within the groups. As we shall see in the chapter on plants and animals, such priorities are almost impossible, because most plants support mixed communities, and all these play a vital role in trout-fishing waters.

In the drawings the water line is not always shown, and plants are not necessarily depicted as they appear in the water. To have drawn them true to their natural positions would have made leaf definition too vague for identification. In general, they are shown as they would look when lifted out of the water and arranged for examination. Many of the features described cannot be made out simply by looking at water plants in their submerged and floating state. Where some species are concerned, the flow of the water bunches stems and foliage and masks the pattern and structure of the leaf, a notable example being mare's-tail. This is one reason why it is easy to confuse certain superficially similar plants if we try to identify them from the river bank instead of removing portions for close inspection.

WATER CROWFOOT, syn Water Buttercup, *Ranunculus* spp: the features common to crowfoot species are white flowers occurring singly, ie one flower per stalk, held at $\frac{1}{2}$in to 1in or so above water, and submerged stems carrying finely divided, generally thread-like leaves. The leaves are invariably branched in greater or lesser degree according to species, sometimes with primary divisions into pairs and secondaries into threes. Except for a few species having rigid segments, the leaves are flexible and generally plume-like in outline. Some species have submerged and floating leaves. The latter are quite distinct, being truly leaflike. They are lobed, toothed, and mainly kidney-shaped, but again certain specific variations in leaf form occur. Submerged leaves of the flexible type collapse when lifted out of the water.

It is appropriate to start at the upper reaches where, in chalk streams, but not in streams fed by rain and hill run-off, we shall find the Chalk Stream Crowfoot, *R. calcareus*, a rather bushy plant with stems 2–6ft long and no floating leaves. The foliage is usually dark green and shows up well in the clear headwaters of chalk streams.

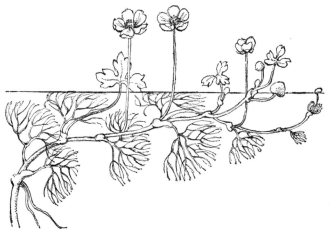

Fig 2   Common Water Crowfoot

It comprises many short segments. I have seen examples in the little feeder streams of the Kennet and Lambourne valleys and in the headwaters of the Itchen where these flow across Hinton Marsh. The flowers have crowded stamens and are large for the water crowfoots, being 35mm in diameter. They appear from April to June.

As a species more typical of the plants generally, we may take the more widely ranging Common Water Crowfoot, *R. aquatalis* (Fig 2). This occurs in our Minnow Reach waters and grows also in still water. There are floating leaves, not generally abundant until some time in June. The stems are about 1–3ft long, and submerged leaves have many long, flexible segments, except in the variety *radians*, which has rigid segments. The flowers are 14mm diameter with few stamens, and appear from May to July.

The Long-leaved Water Crowfoot, *R. fluitans*, is found in the middle and lower reaches of fast streams. It is a strong plant with stems sometimes reaching 10ft. There are no floating leaves. Submerged leaves are characterised by having thick but comparatively few segments, which are long. The flowers are 30mm diameter with few stamens, and appear from May to July.

The Floating Water Crowfoot, *R. pseudofluitans*, is associated with rivers of relatively strong currents. It is abundant in the larger chalk streams of southern England and is perhaps the commonest crowfoot species of the Itchen. It is a strong plant with stems 2–8ft long, with dark green submerged leaves that are flexible and fairly short, being about half the length of those of *fluitans*. Floating leaves are present by June. The flowers are 35mm diameter, with crowded stamens, and appear from June to August.

Another widely ranging species is the Pond Water Crowfoot, *R. peltatus*, appearing in flowing and still waters. It has stems 1–3ft long with submerged leaves composed of long, thin, but rather rigid segments, and floating leaves that appear early in the season. The flowers are 20mm diameter with few stamens, and appear from April to early July.

The most unusual of the flowing water crowfoots is the Bushy-leaved, *R. sphaerospermus* (Fig 3). As its popular name implies, the submerged leaves are not of the general plume-like outline of the others, but are roundish, and composed of many short segments that give a bushy outline. These leaves are dark green. There are no floating leaves. This species is not, I think, very common, but is found chiefly in chalky waters, and then not abundantly. The flowers are 25mm diameter with many stamens, and appear throughout the main summer period.

In still waters and canals there appears the neatest of all the water crowfoots, the Rigid-leaved, *R. circinatus* (Fig 4), whose submerged leaves consist of short, firm segments that radiate from a central point to give a floating disc arrangement. This is

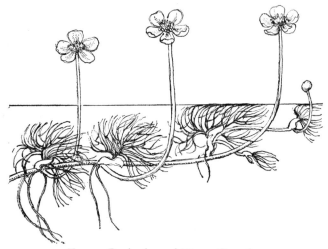

FIG 3   Bushy-leaved Water Crowfoot

quite distinctive and cannot be confused with the foliage of any other species. I have seen it in the Old Barge canal below Winchester and in very slow stretches of Minnow Reach waters in Gloucestershire. Its foliage is not adapted to strong currents and I have not seen it in even the slow reaches of chalk streams, but

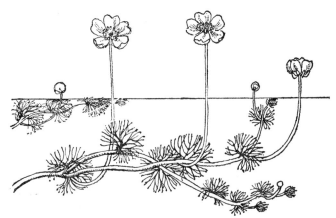

FIG 4   Rigid-leaved Water Crowfoot

Page 53   PLATE 6   A stony and mainly plantless trout brook

PLATE 7 Algal growth and broad-leaved pond-weed severely encroaching upon a trout pond

that does not necessarily mean that it is never found in these. It has no floating leaves. The stems are 30in long, the flowers 15mm diameter with many stamens. They appear from June to August.

These are the principal species of the genus as far as the fly fisher is concerned. The last named is, in fact, very much on the borderline, because its waters are normally too slow for trout in the prime of life, and most of the specimens inhabiting such waters are elderly and inedible, and have gone into a well-earned retreat.

Before we leave these plants we might just note how stem length is related to the type of water in which the species is growing. The stronger the flow, the longer the stem, is the general pattern. Thus the Chalk Stream species, growing high upstream in the infant waters, has an average stem length of 4ft; the Long-leaved species, taking a force of water many times that of the upstream end, has a maximum stem some two and a half times longer than the average for *calcareus* and four times that of the Rigid-leaved, which occupies very quiet waters. We may also find that species which occupy both still and flowing water will have shorter stems in the former and longer ones in the latter.

The difficulties of nomenclature which occasionally obtain with a genus having a large number of different forms, sometimes with only slight variations between them, are not entirely absent from the water crowfoots. For example, *peltatus* has two forms, the one described above, and another which is a much sparser and less common plant, found at the edges of ponds that have a sandy bed. The first is, I believe, more generally called *penicillatus*, and as this is considered by many botanists to be the one of which *pseudo-fluitans* is a variety, the distinction is probably appropriate, since the rarer form of *peltatus* is not a plant of flowing water, whereas the common form, together with *pseudofluitans*, does grow in flowing water.

WATER CELERY, syn Marshwort, *Apium nodiflorum* (Fig 5): this plant is found in flowing and still water. In the former it is generally rooted in the quiet areas under banks, but its submerged

D

foliage frequently extends into the current margins. Its branched, striated stems are somewhat straggling. They are 1–2ft long. In spite of the common name, the foliage is not particularly celery-like, and is definitely less so than that of the wild celery of salt marshes, *A. graveolens*. The leaf is technically compound, ie composed of leaflets all growing from a single leaf stalk. These are arranged in pairs along the stalk, with a single apical leaflet. The leaflets of each pair are directly opposite on the stalk, and do not themselves have stalks, but grow directly from the main one. Leaflets are lanceolate and irregularly toothed. It is necessary to distinguish between the fruit of water celery and of the next plant, since in other respects the two plants are superficially similar. But first the flowers must be briefly described.

These are white, 3mm in diameter, and appear in clusters of five

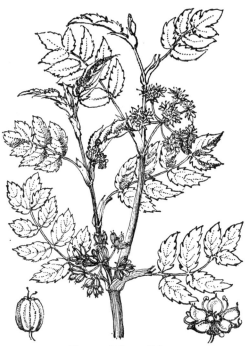

FIG 5   Water Celery

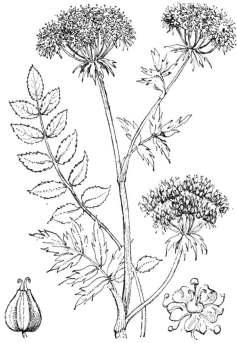

FIG 6   Lesser Water Parsnip

to eight on the tips of short stalks all springing from a common base. This type of inflorescence is an umble, as in wild parsley, hemlock, cow parsnip, to name three of the most common representatives of the family, *Umbelliferae*. The fruit of water celery is technically described as orbicular, ie orb shaped. It has five ridges and in each groove of these is an oil gland known as a vitta. These are not easy to see unless the fruit is cut in half in transverse section with a razor blade or scalpel, and then viewed under a lens. The flowers appear from July to August on emergent stems up to 2ft high.

LESSER WATER PARSNIP, *Sium erectum* (Fig 6), occupies the same position in the water as the above plant. Its stems and foliage are apparently similar (though not actually). Leaflets, as with celery, have no leaf stalks. The obvious difference is in the fruits. Those of parsnip are bulbous, or bulb-shaped. Flowers appear from July to September. There is a completely submerged, non-flowering form.

MARE'S-TAIL, *Hippuris vulgaris* (Fig 7) occurs in static and slow flowing water. It is fairly widely ranging, though preferring alkaline waters. It can make dense beds, but these do not often cover wide areas. Submerged stems are up to 3½ft long, carrying dark green, narrow, flexible leaves 12–15 in long and arranged in whorls, and with wavy margins. Emergent stems arise 6–12 in above the water, with non-flexible leaves, 5–7 in long, with straight margins. An example is shown on the right in the drawing.

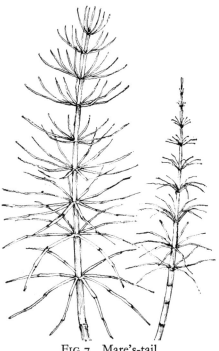

SPIKED WATER MILFOIL, *Myriophyllum spicatum* (Fig 8), grows most strongly in chalky waters, though it is found in many streams

FIG 7   Mare's-tail

and still waters throughout the country. It has submerged stems varying in length from 1ft to 9ft, bearing dark green leaves in whorls mainly of four, though whorls of odd-numbered leaves sometimes occur. The leaves are segmented and in outline have a herringbone pattern. Segments vary from thirteen to

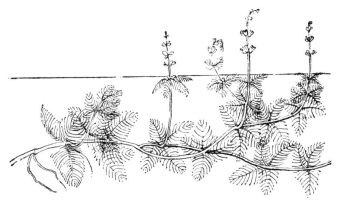

FIG 8   Spiked Water Milfoil

thirty-five. An emergent stalk that rises 1–3in above the water bears small, red, inconspicuous flowers, 1mm diameter, and in whorls. They appear from June to August. An associated species is *M. alterniflorum*, differing only in having fewer leaf segments.

Another plant with leaves of a herringbone pattern is WATER VIOLET, *Hottonia palustris* (Fig 9), found in static and slow-flowing water. This is easily confused with milfoil, but a fairly definite distinction is the lighter green of its leaves. Also the leaf arrangement is less distinctly whorled. In fact, there are no exact whorls; the arrangement is better described as spiral. The flower stem reaches higher above water than that of milfoil, and the flowers are pale lilac, appearing from May to June.

STARWORT, *Callitriche stagnalis* (Fig 10), grows in static and flowing water. It has thin submerged stems 6–36in long with light green leaves arranged in pairs at intervals along the stalk, the leaves of each pair being opposite and growing out direct from the stem, without leaf stalks. The general leaf shape is narrow and spathulate, but lower leaves are narrower than higher ones. The emergent portions are seen as small rosettes of leaves, slightly

FIG 9   Water Violet

FIG 10   Starwort

above the water. Small but dense mats of starwort often appear on the surface of ponds, and also in close association with other plants.

WATERCRESS, *Nasturtium officinale*, syn *Rorippa Nasturtium—aquaticum*, is common in the upper reaches of chalk streams and in these waters generally, and occurs widely in clean, running water. It has thickish, glabrous stems rooted in the stream bed but rising above water level to about 1ft, though occasionally higher. Stems are much branched. Leaves are compound, with generally two pairs of leaflets and a terminal leaflet, except the lower ones, which are often composed of one pair and one terminal. These lower ones are often stalked, though not invariably, but the higher are unstalked. Generally, the terminal leaflet is larger and more heart-shaped than the lateral ones, which are elliptical. The foliage is dark green and has the strong flavour of cultivated watercress. Some terminal leaflets are elliptical, but still larger than the lateral ones.

PONDWEEDS, *Potamogeton*, spp, occur in static water and in slow stretches of flowing water. The Broad-leaved, *P. natans* (Fig 11), is among the most common. The floating leaves are broadly elliptical, somewhat leathery, and variable in size, sometimes being 5in long and half as wide across the centre, and are long-stalked. They are visibly purplish, a feature which at once identifies the species. Submerged leaves are much narrower, and have a stalk-like rather than a leaf-like appearance.

Shining Pondweed, *P. lucens*, is easily distinguished from the above by its very short leaf stalks, and the vivid green leaf colour. The leaves are large, elliptical, and taper at both ends. Leaf margins are frequently wavy.

The Curled Pondweed, *P. crispus* is completely submerged. The leaves are linear-oblong with wavy margins, and no leaf stalks. The plant is usually tinged reddish, a factor which is especially noticeable at leaf tips and bases.

FIG 11   Broad-leaved Pondweed

The Perfoliate Pondweed, *P. perfoliatus* (Fig 12), has bluntly oval leaves, tapering at the tips, and arranged in a clearly alternate pattern along the stem, without leaf stalks.

In addition to nine floating Potamogeton pondweeds with mainly broad leaves, of which the above are those most likely to interest fly fishers, there are ten species with grass-like leaves. The most widely occurring is the Fennel-leaved, *P. pectinatus* (Fig 13). This has narrow, usually dark green leaves on many-branched stems. The leaves are distinctly grass-like, tapering to a sharp point, with a sheath at the base growing direct from the stem, without a leaf stalk. This species often grows densely just below the surface of ponds and the quiet stretches of running water.

For identification purposes, the foliage of these pondweeds is sufficient. It is sometimes encrusted with lime, as a result of calcium carbonate deposits resulting from dissolution of calcium bicarbonate.

The flowers, which are generally small and borne on emergent stalks, are variable in arrangement and not essential for general

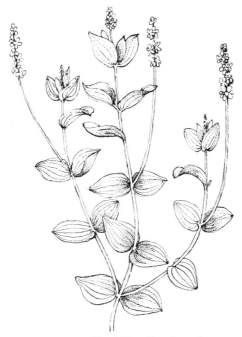

FIG 12   Perfoliate Pondweed

identification, but it is worth mentioning that the flower stem of Shining Pondweed thickens at its upper end, whereas the flower stems of the other species do not thicken.

CANADIAN PONDWEED, *Elodea canadensis* (Fig 14), is an introduced species, having arrived in England from North America. It became notorious as a weed pest throughout the period roughly from 1860 to 1880. It is recorded as having been introduced to the

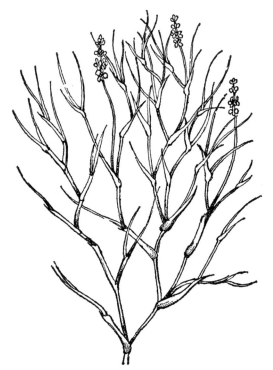

FIG 13   Fennel-leaved Pondweed

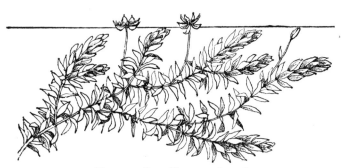

FIG 14   Canadian pondweed

Oxford Botanic Garden in 1849, from where it spread to the Thames at Folly Bridge. William Baxter, curator of the Oxford Botanic Garden, noticed in 1853 that in a ditch in the Long Meadow the plant had formed 'an uninterrupted dense mass from one end of the ditch to the other'. By about 1860 it had made parts of the Thames almost impassable, and was a serious threat to many rivers and canals. Spread is by fragmentation, and growth of winter buds.

Canadian pondweed has declined substantially since its heyday. It is still widespread but seldom abundant enough to cause trouble.

It has long, branched, flexible stems bearing small elliptical leaves which are usually down curved at the tips. They are dark green, in whorls of three, though sometimes two or four leaves are found to a whorl. There are no leaf stalks. The plant grows up to the water surface, but the leaves do not emerge. This pond-weed is quite distinct from the *Potamogeton* species, and is unlikely to be confused with these.

With the possible exception of Fennel-leaved Pondweed which, because of its structure, offers a relatively small grazing area for the nymphs and larvae of anglers' flies, the plants in the above list are indispensable in fly-fishing waters, as we shall see when we come to the chapter on animal populations. Each species contri-butes in value to the total, and in flourishing waters all of the plants in this list will be found in some area or other, in accordance with their liking for fast, slow, or static water. In chalk streams there will often be a well-mixed plant community occupying quite small areas, and indicating how nature abhors a single species environment, a fact which is being increasingly disregarded in modern crop husbandry. Monocultural systems have often super-seded the older mixed economies, to the undoubted detriment of the soil and the surroundings, though exponents of monoculture seem utterly incapable of grasping the elementary need for crop rotation. However, our present business is water plants, not food growing, so we must get back into our waders.

Having discussed the main flora, we will now turn to the fauna. Later we shall have to consider some more plants, but as this consideration will be in some degree an extension of the chapters on fauna, it must await its turn.

CHAPTER 6

A Background to Nymphs

AS AN introduction to plants and the trout food they carry, we
might ponder on the fact that when the research workers, E.
Percival and H. Whitehead, investigated the faunas of the Yorkshire rivers Aire, Nidd and Wharfe more than forty years ago they
found that in areas of no vegetation the largest number of animals
per sq m was 4,060 on average, and in vegetated areas it was
431,941. Several species were of no interest to fly fishers, but all
were trout food.

Percival and Whitehead were among the pioneers of freshwater
biology in its modern sense, and their findings are still used as a
basis for the wider interpretation of plant-animal relationships in
fresh waters.

Although the substrata and most of the plants they studied were
types that are largely outside those dealt with here, the Perfoliate
Pondweed was included, and this carried a total of 243,972 animals
per sq m. Of these, 3,450 were *Ephemeroptera* nymphs, 3,196 were
stonefly nymphs, 2,930 were caddis larvae. *Diptera* species
totalled 230,400, of which 203,200 were midge larvae, and
27,200 were larvae of blackflies, ie presumably reed smuts. The
remainder were mites, snails, beetles and limpets. Stonefly
nymphs are less numerous in lowland waters and in any case are a
mixed blessing, since the larger species are carnivorous on the
nymphs of anglers' flies.

Most of the nymphs were composed of *Baëtis* species, and one
species of *Ephemerella*. This was possibly Blue-winged Olive, *E.
ignita* (Fig 15), but might have been the Yellow Evening Dun,
E. notata, which likes alkaline streams.

The highest total recorded, ie 431,941, was on thick moss. The figures demonstrate the value of certain plants which are often taken by the fly fisher to be of no account. Indeed, in the case of the pondweed, the figures illustrate the value of a plant that is too easily regarded by those who fish expensive chalk streams as an interloper among the plant community.

The plantless zones studied by Percival and Whitehead were substrata of stones, varying between the stable and the unstable. We are not concerned with such stream beds, but it is of interest

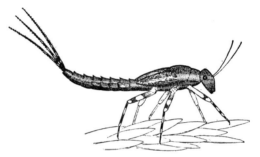

FIG 15   Nymph of Blue-winged Olive,
Ephemerella ignita, 9mm long, from life

to consider them briefly in relation to plantless zones of Minnow Reach waters where bankside trees are too dense, and where shade is too heavy for the sturdy growth of higher plants.

The total number of *Ephemeroptera* nymphs for the eroding or partially eroding substrata as a whole was 2,301 per sq m. Small as this was in comparison with the total number for vegetated zones, it was nevertheless a good value in terms of the particular environment, but it would be most optimistic to imagine that a similar one would obtain in plantless zones of Minnow Reach streams.

We cannot relate the two environments, for they are totally different. In stony streams there is always oxygen freely available and there are always nymph species that are adapted to turbulent conditions and to the utilisation of the oxygen provided by these.

In plantless Minnow Reach waters oxygen in sufficient quantities to satisfy the nymphs is not freely available because the water is usually too slow to supply it, and the supply on which nymphs depend can be present in the main only if plants are present. Even those nymph species adapted to relatively slow water, and which do not have mobile gill plates for activating the flow, will not survive long without adequate oxygen. They will invariably be found on areas of plants only an inch or two away from the current, though the colonised portion may be relatively calm.

The absence of higher plants from turbulent, rocky streams is a natural phenomenon. Such plants have no place in these streams, but compensating factors ensure the existence of nymphs, and also trout, small though the latter are. The absence of plants in Minnow Reach waters is more likely to be due to factors which are distinctly unacceptable to fly fishermen. These may be unsuitable substrata, lack of sunlight, excessive deposits of foliage, or turbidity of water, all of which are capable of adjustment.

The unsatisfactory chemical conditions that may arise in plantless zones are an aggravating factor extremely difficult, if not impossible, to correct by any single, direct method, but equally capable of being rectified by general improvement.

Plantless zones of Minnow Reach waters can definitely be short of nymphs and reed smut larvae. The stone-clinging types will not be very evident because they belong essentially to well aerated waters, and the stones on the bed of plantless Minnow Reach waters are not usually sufficiently washed, or washed swiftly enough, to ensure good aeration.

In Minnow Reach zones which are not plantless, but which contain mainly mosses and pondweeds, we should not expect to find animal communities comparable with those found by Percival and Whitehead. The pondweed on which they based their records was growing in stony substrata, which suggests a moderately swift flow with the oxygenating properties associated with this. These substrata, together with the water speed, would combine to give characteristics of Tansley's Zone 3, and there were probably other plants like crowfoots, which appear in Zone 3.

The pondweeds are, in fact, good oxygenating plants, and their presence in otherwise plantless areas probably ensures enough oxygen to sustain moderate populations of those nymphs which are less demanding of oxygen, or which create micro-currents round their bodies by means of their gill plates and by rapid lateral movements of their abdomen, as in the case of the *Baëtis* species.

Several modern workers have said that much remains to be discovered about plant-animal relationships, particularly as to why certain animals frequent certain plants in preference to others. In some instances the reason, or part of the reason, seems clear, and will be discussed in the next chapter. I had originally intended to combine this with the foregoing, but on reflection I think perhaps any extension of this present chapter would prove hard on the digestion, so I suggest we consume its contents, digest them if we can, and then come with an easy stomach to the main consideration of the plants and the animals.

Page 71 PLATE 8 A well-managed waterside, with firm walking and
good herbage to provide cover for the angler

Page 72 PLATE 9
(*left*) Watercress
choking a trout
brook;
PLATE 10 (*right*)
hemp agrimony just
coming into flower

CHAPTER 7

Plants and Animals in Detail

BROADLY SPEAKING, the relationships that are known to exist between aquatic plants and animals may be associated with the physical needs of the fauna and the ways in which the different plants supply these. Some organisms must have constant supplies of oxygen; for others the chief demand is shelter from the current, and possibly from sunlight and predators. Others again are so constituted that they can live in conditions of diminished oxygen. Notable examples are the bloodworms, ie the larvae of certain Chironomids. Their blood contains haemoglobin, which gives them a red colour. This absorbs oxygen, which is stored within the larvae and released for use if the oxygen of the water becomes very low. The larvae can therefore live in water that is heavily polluted and in which fish and vast numbers of aquatic species could not survive.

By contrast, all nymphs of the anglers' flies and a great many larvae of *Diptera* need oxygen concentrations within the high range, with the perhaps single exception of the Pond Olive, *Cloëon dipterum* (Fig 16), which inhabits small areas of water that reach relatively high summer temperatures and are considerably lower in dissolved oxygen than are lakes and flowing waters.

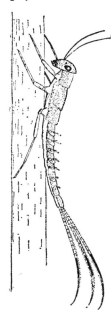

FIG 16 Nymph of Pond Olive, *Cloëon dipterum*, 6mm long, (half grown), from life

As a measure of security against predators, many aquatic species have developed camouflage colours which presumably render the animals less conspicuous when their favoured habitat is an exposed one. Reed smut larvae, for example, are green, or drab coloured, as are various other plant dwellers, though to what extent this saves them from trout is not known. In some instances camouflage takes the form of an apparent similarity in shape between a larva and the part of a plant it inhabits, such as the leaf stipule.

We will now take the plants individually and examine the plant-host associations. For ease of reference and in spite of repetition, I will again give popular and botanical names.

All species of Crowfoot, *Ranunculus*, that grow in strongly flowing water may be regarded as principal hosts to the larvae of Reed Smuts, *Simulium* spp, the adults of which are also known as Buffalo Gnats (from the USA), as Blackflies (Fig 17), and as Black Gnats. All terms are descriptive, though vague, and the last is unfortunate, since it creates confusion with the quite distinct species, *Bibio johannis*, which is not aquatic, but terrestrial, and whose association with water is adventitious. This is the one for which the name Black Gnat should be reserved.

It has been recorded that at peak periods populations of reed smut larvae on crowfoot in fast water in the Itchen may be present at the rate of about 120 per gm dry weight of plant. In 1930 White-head found that reed smut larvae composed 27 per cent of the animals on samples of crowfoot from the Yorkshire chalk stream, the Driffield Beck. We will keep this stream in mind, because it typifies the northern equivalent of many south country chalk streams, and is fairly distinct from the more torrential waters of typical trout becks.

The larvae inhabit those parts of the plant most directly washed by the current, ie the portions of the fronds that wave in the water. They do not feed on the algal covering, but on minute particles of algae carried by the current, which they absorb through extremely fine, hairlike filtering appendages arranged as a pair of plumes.

The plant is merely a support to which the larva attaches itself by means of a posterior sucker. The larva possesses a proleg, and by the alternate use of this and the sucker, it moves about the

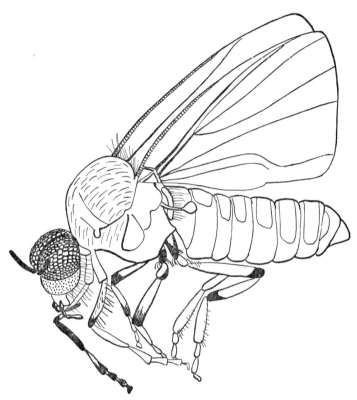

FIG 17   Adult of Male Reed Smut, *Simulium ornatum*. (Enlarged.)
Wings are slightly foreshortened

plant in a looping motion, very much in the manner of looper caterpillars. Flowing water is essential for reed smut larvae; it carries their food, provides oxygen, and keeps their filtering fans in motion. In still water these collapse, when the larvae will quickly perish.

Modern research has established that there is a fairly distinct pattern of movement of larvae along crowfoot fronds as these extend during the growing season into the currents, and as the basal areas become silted up in varying degrees. This pattern can be related to development of the larvae. In winter, crowfoot foliage largely dies down and larvae must seek their territory among the basal regions, which become washed free of silt, when the foliage dies away and so no longer diverts the current away from the basal portions. Populations normally start to appear on the leaves in February or March, as the young foliage begins to grow out. With the gradual increase of silt at the basal end of the plant, and consequently a slower flow over this part, the larvae move along the growing fronds. By about late March there will be well developed specimens concentrated towards the apical ends of the fronds, with younger ones in the rear. The latter presumably need less food and less oxygen than the former, and their simpler needs would be met in the lower oxygen area of the plant base.

In fact, we can discern an excellent natural dispensation in this arrangement. Although the younger larvae are upstream of their elder brethren, they do not compete for the food that is coming down on the current. For one thing their appetite is less than that of the more developed specimens; for another, the latter are not immediately in front and thus not in the same line of flow, but are strung out at an angle to the plant axis, on the growing fronds.

This pattern will continue right through to late May or early June, with larvae building up to peak numbers until the pupal and finally the adult fly stage is reached. There will, of course, be fluctuations in numbers along the fronds, owing to the various times at which individuals reach maturity and fly off, and there may be marked seasonal fluctuations overall, but in general we may safely conclude that crowfoot in running water will support large average populations of reed smut larvae. September is often a good month to look for them, since it is a period of high production in some seasons.

I have mentioned specific adaptations among reed smut larvae in connection with stone-clinging types; such references are perhaps of only academic interest in practical fly fishing, but it is worth distinguishing between stone and plant clingers. Two of the latter are *S. reptans* and *S. equinum*.

The fly fisher's most important flies are of course those of the *Ephemeroptera* order. We find certain of these present on crowfoot. *R. fluitans*, in particular, seems to be well favoured by nymphs of Large Dark Olive, *Baëtis rhodani*, the adults of which are among the earliest flies to appear (Fig 18). Here we have another good example of how a species will select a plant that provides essential oxygen, or is growing in a stream area where oxygen is guaranteed. Large Dark Olive nymphs are high oxygen users, yet their gill plates are not designed, as are those of other species, for movement to aerate the water. They are fixed and so the nymph cannot create a current for itself, but relies on the constant flow of water over its body. The body is streamlined to ensure this. Neither are the nymphs as efficient swimmers as some other types. Thus nature so arranges things that the nymphs have in crowfoot a suitable feeding ground in a well aerated position from which travel is unnecessary.

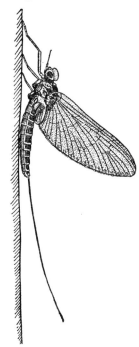

FIG 18 Female subimago (dun) of Large Dark Olive, *Baëtis rhodani*, in resting position × 3·5

It has been found that at peak periods Large Dark Olive nymphs on crowfoot can reach about 20 per gm of weed, a figure probably reached also by Blue-winged Olive, *Ephemerella ignita* (Fig 15). This species inhabits the thicker areas of the plant near the base, where the current is diverted by the root mass and where calmer conditions prevail, but it is never more than an inch or two away from the oxygenating influence of the current. It is an inhabitant of the current margins, rather than of the full current. Its adaptability to thick vegetation takes the form of small, close-fitting gill plates which do not become entangled with the herbage. It has strong legs, to enable it to move easily among dense growth.

The more freely washed portions of crowfoot sought by Large Dark Olive nymphs are shared with nymphs of the Iron Blue, *Baëtis pumilus* (Fig 19), and with several others of the family. In south-country chalk streams in particular we shall find the Medium Olive, *B. vernus*, and in most parts of the country there should be the other form of Medium Olive, *B. tenax*. The Pale Watery, *B. bioculatus*, will appear on most of the southern chalk streams, and in perhaps smaller numbers on crowfoot in other streams. In the Driffield Beck the nymphs of these anglers' flies in general accounted for about 16 per cent of total animals on crowfoot.

Plant-living species of caddis larvae occur on crowfoot. One of the most important of the adult caddis flies in fly fishing is the Grannom, *Brachycentrus subnubilus*. The term plant-living really means plant-supported, since the larvae attach themselves to the plant and absorb their food as it flows past.

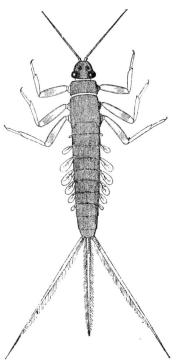

FIG 19   Nymph of Iron Blue, *Baëtis pumilus*

There is considerable variation in living habits among caddis larvae, according to species—some occupying river beds, some among moss and other plants, some under stones, and so on. The river-bed dwellers live within portable cases; other types spin webs to stones, others again do not make cases. I have seldom found any species except the Grannom on crowfoot, but I do not know whether this experience is general. In the Driffield Beck caddis larvae rated only 2 per cent of total animals on crowfoot.

Midge larvae, in complete contrast, rated 43 per cent, and there is no doubt that in some seasons these larvae make up a high percentage of crowfoot fauna, though many species in both larval and adult forms are useless to anglers. The term midge covers many species of the *Diptera*, or true fly order. In general, only those midges in the genus *Chironomus* are of interest to fishermen, and these are largely restricted to the well known lake species like the Olive and Green Midge, *Chironomus tentans* and *C. viridis* respectively, at least as far as specific identification and representation are concerned. There are many other species which few fishermen would recognise, but which can be represented in the pupal stage by one or two general patterns, but of course that is stepping outside the bounds of nymph- and dry-fly fishing.

However limited in their fly-fishing uses the midges on crowfoot are, their presence bespeaks a good oxygen content, since most of them, in company with the reed smut larvae, which belong to the same order, require plenty of this.

A regular inhabitant of crowfoot is the freshwater shrimp, *Gammarus pulex*. This, again, does not interest dry-fly men, but as it is basic trout food of a high order, and as its distribution on water plants follows an interesting pattern, we cannot exclude it.

This shrimp is an excellent example of the ability of a freshwater animal to live dangerously, or at least in the presence of danger, and yet to survive. For a water-bound creature, it is a poor swimmer, and cannot withstand strong currents. Because of this it will rarely venture into fast water, yet it occupies not only the slow water crowfoot species but the fast ones as well, like *R. fluitans* and *R. pseudofluitans*. It changes its position on the plant in accordance with its need to escape the current. Thus the main area of colonisation is the plant base, but if the level of the current alters, and washes over the basal area, the shrimps will descend to lower regions, so that the flow passes above them, or if it strikes at these lower regions, the shrimps will go above it.

They do not colonise fast-water crowfoot in very large numbers; usually about 8 per gm of weed seems to be the average figure so far established for the Itchen, but we must remember that numbers alone do not always determine the value of a species as trout food. Size and weight may be more important, not only nutritionally but also because the fish expends far less energy in capturing one large animal than in capturing many small ones to give the same weight of food. For example, it has been estimated that a trout would have to eat something like 300 of the smallest chironomid larvae to consume the same weight of food provided by one large sedge fly. But the trout seems to be a good trade unionist, for he never works harder for his living than he must, and rather than go grubbing after chironomid larvae in their burrows in the mud, he waits until the pupal stage is reached, when his prey is a hanging target just below the water surface.

Shrimps are by no means confined to the plant bases. In large rivers like the Test and Itchen, subsidiary currents may have more influence on the disposition of shrimps than main ones, and it is quite common to find shrimps on crowfoot fronds at certain times in the summer when surface currents are weaker than deeper ones. In the Driffield Beck, shrimps made up 8 per cent of the fauna of crowfoot.

Closely associated with shrimps are the water snails, *Mollusca*. These, together with shrimps, give trout the pink flesh and red haloes to their spots, which are a mark of high quality. Snails do not seem abundant on crowfoot, and were not found among the Driffield Beck plants, but they certainly occur in the Itchen, though perhaps at no higher rate than about one or two per gm of weed.

On average, larvae of reed smuts and other *Diptera* probably comprise something like 70 per cent of the fauna of crowfoot; *Ephemeroptera* nymphs 15 per cent; shrimps 8 per cent. The remainder are made up of worms, snails, leeches, caddis larvae and mites.

Crowfoot offers less shelter for trout than that afforded by larger leaved plants, but its fine, segmented submerged foliage, through which water passes freely, is ideal for nymphs and larvae, so the plant provides a valuable feeding ground. Also, the soft foliage enables trout to move easily among the beds.

In Water Celery, *Apium nodiflorum*, we have one of the fly fisher's most valuable plants. Its roots are in mostly slack water, but its foliage frequently extends into the current, and as the leaves are relatively large they offer a considerable surface area for grazing fauna. Thus on its slack water portions the plant supports species needing shelter, and on its extended portions those needing flowing water.

As a supporter of *Ephemeroptera* nymphs, celery is in a class by itself, sometimes sustaining at peak periods the same numbers per gm of weed as it sustains of reed smut larvae, which can be about a hundred. Unfortunately, it was not included in the Driffield Beck survey, but samples from the Itchen have been well documented. Celery and crowfoot offer interesting examples of plants of basically different habit which carry two types of animals each of which requires similar living conditions. Crowfoot has thin flexible leaves offering no resistance to the current; celery is a stiffer plant with larger leaves and does resist the current in some degree. We know that nymphs and reed smut larvae need a good current and plenty of oxygen. The fact that both colonise in large numbers plants of different habit is somewhat puzzling.

An assumption could be that by offering some resistance to the flow, celery creates an ideal micro-habitat for oxygen production in the immediate vicinity of the animals, and also that the temporarily resisted flow forms small accumulations of water which hold the minute algae needed by reed smut larvae.

The grazing area, though relatively large on celery, could be smaller in total, weight for weight of plant, than on crowfoot, since the finely divided leaves of the latter may present a larger total surface area. It is a fairly well-established fact that plants with finely divided foliage contain, in general, bigger communities and more species than do plants with larger entire leaves, though celery seems an exception. Judging by Percival and Whitehead, this principle would seem to extend even to moss for, as we have seen, the thick moss carried an average total of 431,941 animals per sq m as against 243,972 for the pondweeds.

Celery supports shrimps in its lower areas at a comparatively high rate, possibly 16 per gm of weed at peak, and small numbers of snails. Some investigators have found it carrying easily the greatest total number of animals in chalk streams, in some cases well over twice the total found on the least populated, namely starwort.

Lesser Water Parsnip, *Sium erectum*, is a betwixt and between plant in fly-fishing waters. It has a good shrimp value, often about 30 per cent of total animals, but is apt to be low in nymphs, at about 10 per cent, and is sometimes devoid of reed smut larvae, or may seldom carry worthwhile numbers. It rates about 10 per cent for the larvae of other *Diptera*, and about 12–15 per cent for assorted worms, together with a few leeches and caddis larvae.

Thus its dry fly and nymph value is more or less confined to comparatively small numbers of *Ephemeroptera*. Their small numbers may be due to the fact that only about half the plant is washed; the other half is erect, and thus the forage area for creatures that must be in permanent contact with the water is somewhat limited.

In water parsnip we have a plant whose value in fly fishing is, on the whole, indirect, rather than direct. Its high shrimp rating makes it a trout larder of first importance, a sort of basic food plant in a trout fishery. We can easily see how, if fly-producing plants were lacking, trout would have little inclination to rise, especially if starwort were also present. Their diet would be composed almost exclusively of shrimps, snails and other forms that do not become flies. This happens much more frequently than anglers sometimes realise. At least they realise that the fish are not rising, and they correctly attribute this to lack of flies, but they do not always appreciate that the dearth of flies is due to a dearth of plants that support nymphs.

This frustrating situation is quite common along slower reaches of Minnow Reach waters, and I know at least one stream on which anglers have resigned themselves to worms and the wet fly, in spite of the fact that the water has an excellent dry-fly potential, which could be realised and made actual if the right type of stream improvements were made, and if nymph-bearing plants were then introduced.

We should certainly not regard water parsnip as a poor sort of plant, associated with dull waters. It grows in the Driffield Beck, which is one of the finest trout streams in the country. Whitehead found it there in company with crowfoot and mare's-tail, and the fauna he recorded on these plants showed a well-mixed fly-fishing community. Of 3,164 animals on parsnip, approximately 316 were nymphs, 1,000 were shrimps; of 3,876 on mare's-tail, 970 were nymphs, 550 were shrimps; of 4,220 on crowfoot, 700 were nymphs, 320 were shrimps. So between them, the plants provided a nymph total of 1,986, and a shrimp total of 1,870. There were about 938 caddis larvae all told, and 6,840 midge larvae. The bare figures might suggest an excessive preponderance of midge larvae, but those which provide acceptable trout food made up probably no more than the numbers which obtain generally in trout waters, and the greatest attraction would have lain among the nymphs.

Mare's-tail, *Hippuris vulgaris*, is sometimes regarded as more of a nuisance than a blessing, and is apt to be thought of as an encroaching plant in almost the same category as Canadian pond-weed. In fact, although it is often dense, it does not usually occupy large areas. Its flexibility makes it an excellent plant for sheltering trout. It is also an injustice to Canadian pondweed to regard it as an encroaching plant, for it has long since learnt its place.

We have seen that water snails do not occupy in large numbers the plants so far dealt with. In mare's-tail the balance is righted. Snails may represent something like 25 per cent of the trout food, a figure almost achieved by this plant in the Driffield Beck. If the remainder were made up of creatures outside the fly-fisherman's range, mare's-tail would be of little interest in fly fishing, except for its high food-carrying value, but another 25 per cent or so of its animal population is often composed of *Ephemeroptera* nymphs. Many times I have seen Iron Blue duns, *Baëtis pumilus* (Fig 19), emerging from mare's-tail beds, or from their vicinity, when they were pounced upon by trout, thus providing yet another example of nature's dispensation, not only in the matter of trout food, but also in the manner in which a nymph species can adjust to varying conditions.

Since mare's-tail grows mainly, though definitely not exclusively, in slow or even static water, we might think it an unsuitable plant for a nymph that needs plenty of oxygen. But Iron Blue nymphs can live in still water for a time. Anyone who is what Gilbert White called a 'nice observer' will notice that Iron Blue nymphs have a habit, not shared with others of their kind, of swaying from side to side. This is a fairly gentle motion, distinct from the quite vigorous lateral movements which the nymphs also engage in, in common with those of the Olives and the Pale Watery, *B. bioculatus*. J. R. Harris has concluded that this swaying motion ensures constant renewal of the water in the immediate vicinity of the nymphs, thus providing a better supply of oxygen in still water.

There were no reed smut larvae recorded on mare's-tail in the Driffield Beck, and in my experience these are scarce on the plant in chalk streams and in other streams, though they have certainly been noted. It is probable that the usually gentle flow in which the plant grows is not enough to keep the larval plumes activated, or to carry the food down. Midge larvae, however, are often present in fair numbers, and on the Driffield Beck made up 16 per cent of the total count. These were not of much value to fly fishers, being composed of such things as dragonfly larvae, *Odonata*, and those of alder flies, *Sialis*. There will usually be a few caddis larvae, and shrimps can be quite well represented, comprising perhaps 10–15 per cent of total animals.

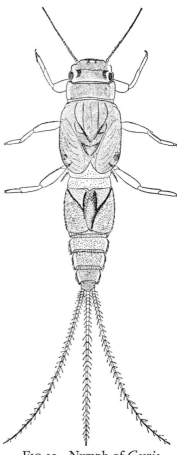

FIG 20   Nymph of *Caenis rivulorum*, 5·5mm long including cerci (tails)

Those least regarded of the *Ephemeroptera*, namely *Caenis* (Figs 20–25), may be strong on mare's-tail, especially *C. macrura*, which likes calm water. The flies are of course known collectively as the 'angler's curse', owing to the enormous numbers in which they frequently appear, when a dry pattern is pretty well swamped by the natural flies. Spinners fall on the water in multitudes, and trout feed voraciously on them in sipping motions, so that the area may show a continual series of gentle rise rings. Only by great luck, or great skill, and with the right pattern, will any fish be caught.

In general terms, I would say that mare's-tail is not an outstanding plant for the fly fisher purely in terms of the species it carries which can be represented, but there can be little doubt that it has considerable value as a trout larder, and so in the wider context of trout fisheries it has a definite claim as a major plant.

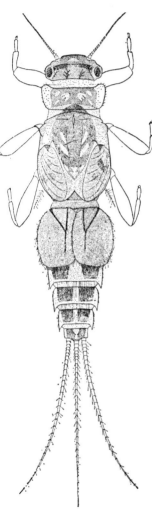

Population figures for Spiked Water Milfoil, *Myriophyllum spicatum*, are sparse, but I do not think there can be any doubt that it supports a useful range of trout food. Being a wide-ranging plant, it will grow in conditions that satisfy such diverse creatures as shrimps and reed smut larvae, and in running water its pliable foliage, offering free access to the current, is colonised by the latter.

But though pliable, the foliage is dense, and we shall often find it populated by nymphs of Blue-winged Olive, which, as we have already noted, are well formed for moving among thick vegetation. The Blue-winged Olive does, of course, belong to a different genus from the general olive tribe; the former is *Ephemerella*, and the latter, *Baëtis*, but members of the tribe will also inhabit this plant, and there will be larvae of caddis and various midges.

Water Violet, *Hottonia palustris*, deserves, I think, a place under

FIG 21   Nymph of *Caenis moesta*, 8mm long including cerci

the heading of main plants, even though it appears to have excited little attention among biologists, and few records of its animal populations exist. The foliage of this completely submerged plant can accommodate good numbers of Blue-winged Olive nymphs, possibly because the combination of leaf structure and slow-flowing water in which the plant grows, offers suitable conditions for these nymphs. The habitat is different from that of crowfoot, but the living conditions for the nymphs have some similarity with those of the faster-water plant. On the latter, the nymphs inhabit areas not directly washed by strong currents, but over which enough water flows to create adequate oxygen supplies; on water violet they are found over the plant surface in general, which suggests that the 'herringbone' structure of the leaves filters enough water to satisfy the nymphs, while the filtering process contributes to aeration.

I have found Water Violet in still waters to be a good home for Pond Olive nymphs, and have long regarded the plant as an essential member of the flora of a trout pond. In still waters there is no regular flow over and around the plants, and we shall not find on them nymphs of any species needing flowing water, but that principle applies in general, and does not lessen the value of Water Violet as a pond plant.

Just as crowfoot is a principal home of reed smut larvae, and celery of nymphs, so is Starwort, *Callitriche stagnalis*, a principal home of shrimps. The way these creatures keep popping up in a book devoted to fly-fishers' plants may seem odd, but as I have already intimated, we cannot evaluate the plants solely according to whether they do or do not provide animals that can be copied by the contents of the dry-fly box. We must consider them in the wider context of a trout fishery, and we must remember that the trout that waxes fat on shrimps does not eat only shrimps. It eats also nymphs, duns and spinners, and should, by the grace of providence or the law of averages, one day fall to our Orange Quill.

The more we examine the plant-host relationships, the more do we see a natural pattern that ensures fair shares for all. Nature provides a suitable territory, a habitat, for each of the myriad species living in freshwater, at least until man with his genius for destruction intervenes.

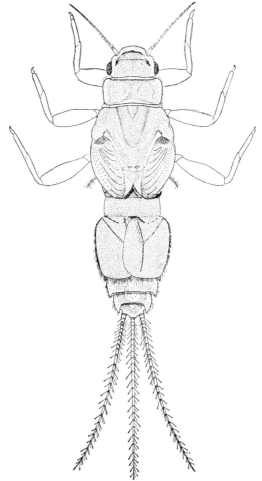

FIG 22   Nymph of *Caenis macrura*, 7mm long including cerci

Starwort provides another pointer to the selectivity practised by plant-living animals in freshwaters. Although the plant remains in leaf over winter, and so might be presumed to offer a more permanent and therefore a more acceptable home than crowfoot, which mainly dies down in winter, it is not colonised to any marked extent by species which inhabit crowfoot, like reed smut larvae, though it can carry as many as fifty *Baëtis* nymphs per gm of weed when it is in flowing water.Presumably such current as it will tolerate would be insufficient for the needs of appreciable numbers of larvae.

Shrimp numbers can reach some twenty-five or so per gm of weed, and snails about five. The first number may also be reached by reed smut larvae, so this plant is by no means rejected by these, but populations are perhaps seldom more than a quarter of those on crowfoot, and are virtually absent from starwort in still water.

Oxygen availability may be a factor governing larval populations on the plant in flowing water. Although oxygen demands of shrimps are less than those of larvae, they are nevertheless quite considerable, and twenty-five shrimps per gm of weed is a significant number for a relatively large animal. Competition among the larvae themselves would also mount, in slow water, to an unacceptable limit if populations became excessive. Starwort can also harbour dragonfly nymphs and alder and caddis-fly larvae.

Its average animal population recorded over a two-season period in the Itchen was found to total ninety-four, ie less than half that on crowfoot and celery. One reason for its smaller populations is probably the simple one of living space and grazing area. Its small leaves obviously cannot provide the same quantity of food or the same elbow room as the leaves of the other two plants.

Watercress, *Nasturtium officinale*, is a plant of great value in trout streams, and its presence indicates good-quality water. I do not know what its toleration limits in regard to pollution are, but it certainly thrives in water of high purity, and the cultivated kinds are grown for market in areas where there are non-polluted waters. It is an ideal harbourage for *Ephemeroptera* nymphs, since it grows

F

in well aerated, running water, and it also makes stands dense enough to provide shelter for shrimps and snails. It can also encroach strongly in the absence of adequate control, especially in narrow streams, where it may reduce the flow to a mere trickle (Plate 9, p 72).

As we have seen from Percival and Whitehead, the Pondweeds, *Potamogeton* spp, can be richly endowed with nymphs. The main genus involved, in my experience, is *Baëtis*, where the plants are in flowing water, and in still water I have found the Claret Dun, *Leptophlebia vespertina*, to be the commonest inhabitant. This dark-coloured nymph is associated almost exclusively with dark waters, or waters over a dark bed; it is common on the slower stretches of Minnow Reach waters where these flow over reddish-coloured deposits like those of Old Red Sandstone, or where pondweed is growing in mud in slow streams and in ponds. The nymphs create a current

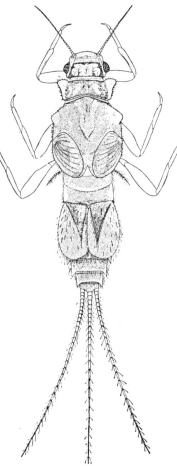

FIG 23   Nymph of *Caenis horaria*, 10mm long including cerci

round their bodies by gill movements. They do not appear to swim far, but move mainly by crawling, and then only slowly. If a leaf bearing a nymph is picked off, and the nymph agitated with one's finger-nail, it will be found that movement is quite sluggish. One of the most effective backgrounds for this nymph is the Broad-leaved Pondweed, *P. natans*, whose purplish leaves provide good camouflage.

In ponds I have found nymphs of Pond Olive, *Cloëon dipterum*, well represented on *Potamogeton* and on Canadian Pondweed, *Elodea canadensis* (which carries also Claret Duns in ponds), but I have not seen Canadian pondweed in many streams—certainly not in chalk streams—carrying much in the way of nymphs, though that is not to say that they are invariably nymphless; more probably, my observation was faulty.

What I have seen time and again is trout feeding avidly on Pond Olive nymphs and chironomid pupae at the edges of beds of Canadian pondweed, and then retiring among the weed. One scorching day in June when I could not summon up enough energy to cast over trout, I sat on the pond bank watching fish chasing the rapidly darting Pond Olive nymphs near Canadian pondweed, and marvelled that, unlike myself, they had so much go in them, for the water must have been almost uncomfortably warm, and I imagined that dissolved oxygen must have been at a low level. I was not able to take the temperature as I had no thermometer, but it could not have been much below 70° F, a value at which trout cannot survive long, let alone expend energy on chasing food, unless the water is fully oxygenated.

I noticed that virtually all the feeding was in areas of Canadian pondweed. Although there was a considerable region of the pond where this weed did not grow, it was almost completely free of visibly feeding trout. This plant is an excellent oxygenator of water, and that was possibly the reason for the heavy trout concentration in its vicinity. The dissolved oxygen would have been very localised, since the water was perfectly still in the area outside that occupied by the trout, and in such circumstances diffusion into that area would have been very slow.

If my deduction was correct, the great value of Canadian

pondweed in still water was well illustrated, and it was evident that my first assumption regarding a low concentration of dissolved oxygen was correct only in respect of the larger pond area where this weed was not growing.

The pondweeds in general do I think, carry a fairly typical fauna; I have found larvae of caddis and reed smuts, as well as the already mentioned olive nymphs, where the *Potamogeton* species were in flowing water, and also dragonfly nymphs and larvae of alder flies. In still water the fauna is less varied, the species of interest to fly fishers being confined mainly to the Claret Dun and Pond Olive and a few caddis larvae. Shrimps I have not found anywhere on pondweeds; whether they give these plants a miss, or whether I have simply missed them, I cannot say. Snails are usually present, in some form or other, in fair numbers. In still waters I have found the tiny bivalve pea mussels, *Sphaerium*, and in still and slow flowing waters, members of *Limnaea*, especially the well-named Wandering Snail, *L. pereger*.

We see, then, that the pondweeds, sometimes cursed by

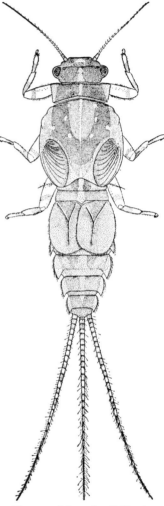

FIG 24 Nymph of *Caenis robusta*, 15mm long including cerci

fishermen, are good plants to have in a trout fishery. Their nymph-bearing capacity can be considerable, numerically, if not in species; they carry numerous other creatures that feed trout, and Canadian pondweed in particular is a valuable producer of oxygen.

At this point we might consider a few plants which do not rate as main species in fly fishing but which merit our attention.

Burr-reed, *Sparganium erectum*, is another plant for which population figures are sparse. As an emergent, it is unlikely to provide living quarters on the scale of submerged plants, but the submerged runners, together with the basal areas of the stems arising from these, can support virtually the same species as the pondweeds, mare's-tail and starwort, though rarely a comparable total number of animals, or a comparable total number within any species. There is also the Unbranched or Simple Burr-reed, *S. simplex*, which has similar harbourage properties.

It is convenient to include with the burr-reeds 'reedy' plants in general—Common Reed, *Phragmites communis*; Great and Lesser Reedmace, *Typha latifolia* and *T. augustifolia*; Bulrush, *Schoenoplectus lacustris*; Sedges, *Carex* spp, and several others of the reed and grass type. Most of these carry a mixed fauna on their submerged positions, the species and the numbers of animals within each being probably generally the same as those on Burr-reed.

These plants occur mainly in slow or static water, and they can cause severe silting if allowed to become too heavily established. They do not really come into the category of fly-fishers' plants, except inasmuch as they support a limited fly-fishing fauna. For one thing, the water in which they grow is usually too silted and shallow for trout, and for another, they cannot be classed as regulators and diverters of currents. Such action as they have on the water is rather an adverse than a beneficial one.

Neither do they provide the water with oxygen, because the oxygen they give off goes into the atmosphere, since the leaves are held above water. The leaves of many emergents are rich in cellulose, the hard substance that makes up the cell walls, and which decomposes with difficulty. Thus the water margins

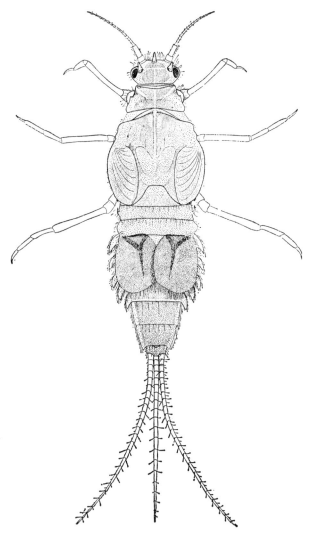

FIG 25 Nymph of *Brachycercus harrisella* (*Caenidae*).
Length from head to tip of abdomen 8·5mm,
to ends of cerci 14mm

become overlaid with fallen leaves that are of little or no value to bacteria and other organisms of decomposition, and the silting process gradually proceeds.

Nevertheless, together with bank herbage, they can fulfil a function that, in certain circumstances, is very useful. If a river is subjected to strong cross winds many emerging duns may be blown away across country, if there is no natural barrier, and even if the flies succeed in mating, which is unlikely in boisterous wind, the spinners may never get back to the water for egg laying. But if there are tall stands of rush etc along stretches of the river's edge, these will catch many wind-blown duns, which will shelter in the herbage until calmer conditions prevail.

We will end this chapter with something that looks like a higher plant, but is an alga, or perhaps I should put all that in the plural, since there are several species. They are known collectively as Stoneworts, *Chara* spp and *Nitella* spp. They are highly developed forms of algae, completely different in appearance from the common 'blanket weeds', and are delicate and even beautiful organisms. They consist of whorls of shoots at regular intervals on a central 'stem', and look exactly like finely dissected leaves. Stoneworts produce not flowers, but male and female spores, which are carried inside spore cases. These cases are known as sporangia; they vary in colour, the most easily seen ones being bright orange. The algae are rooted in the substratum by organs known as rhizoids.

The average height of stoneworts is about 12in. They are green, but, like the pondweeds, may be heavily encrusted with calcium carbonate, when they assume different colourings. They are very brittle and usually feel rough when handled.

Since other forms of algae are a primary food for the freshwater fauna, we would expect stoneworts to support communities, which they do, at least when not coated with lime. The animals found on them are similar to those on pondweeds.

In assessing animal populations, we should appreciate that any single assessment, or any single recording of species, cannot be taken as a general index. For reasons that can hardly ever be fully explained, a stretch of river, or individual weed beds, or areas of beds, that teem with flies one year, may be poor in flies the following year. For example, in 1935 an assessed area of the Bristol Avon had 484 animals per sq m; in 1936 there were 1,964. Again, an area of the Lark with a high calcium content and a muddy bed had 508 animals per sq m, while an area with a stony bed had 3,031, figures which, by all the logic of aquatic relationships, should have been reversed.

But in spite of such variations and seeming anomalies, the fact remains that over a period of years a fairly consistent average will be maintained, provided the water and the plants are properly tended. And where proper tending goes with freedom, or comparative freedom, from pollution, the average will be satisfactory.

CHAPTER 8

Plants Dutiful or Dubious

THERE ARE times when the need to improve the flow of trout streams presents the problem of whether certain plants should not simply be reduced, but should be eliminated. It can be a difficult decision, made more so by the fact that many of the plants that contribute to reduced flow and silt deposits are the valuable ones in terms of fly life, and conversely, some that do not so contribute are not particularly valuable in this respect. Others again that do not impede flow do carry useful animal numbers. Yet another problem is that plants of little fly value may be in positions from which their removal will have no significant effect on the current, and we do not want to rip plants out if such action serves no worthwhile purpose.

But let us imagine for the moment that we are faced with the demand to eliminate a stand of either mare's-tail or the rootless perennial, Hornwort, *Ceratophyllum demersum*. Although rootless, this plant is anchored at its stem base in the river bed, and is completely submerged. It has dark green, threadlike leaves which usually have a 'floatable' or inflated appearance, but are stiff to the touch, and have very small marginal teeth that give them a bristly feel. They appear in distinct whorls, and each whorl has many leaves. From casual observation it is possible to confuse hornwort with mare's-tail, and I have known more than one person to affirm that the latter is a useless nymph-bearing plant, when in fact the plant they were castigating was hornwort.

Hornwort does not attract a flourishing periphyton and therefore attracts few animals. Its leaves do not readily decompose, and so they contribute to silting-up processes. If the choice arose

97

whether to rip out mare's-tail or hornwort, the latter would be the obvious victim. But the plant does possess at least one virtue; it is a good oxygenator, and so should be left for this purpose, if there is no compelling reason for its removal.

Along stream margins where the flow is poor we often find Water Mint, *Mentha aquatica*, or its species, all of which smell of peppermint, especially when bruised. It has long, square stems which are hairy; broad, oval leaves, bluntly pointed, toothed, and also hairy; and conspicuous lilac-coloured flowers in round bunches at the shoot tips, with small, poorly developed ones lower down in the leaf axils.

Water mint is a decorative plant, but of little use to fly fishers. It does have submerged vegetation, but this is not colonised to any extent by fishermen's flies, probably because the substratum in which the plant grows is virtually waterlogged and the micro climate must be poor in oxygen. Water mint is an almost certain sign of conditions in its immediate region which no trout will tolerate. It does not necessarily create the conditions, but exploits them, and in doing so, aggravates them. Any appreciable marginal stretch of this plant is a stretch lost to the bank liers, which is a great pity, for some of the best trout lie under the banks. Here, then, is a definite call for eradication and for mud scooping, in order to improve the marginal bed and to get the water moving under the banks.

In the many little wandering brooks that feed the rivers of the chalk valleys and pastoral landscapes, we shall find Brooklime, *Veronica beccabunga*, a water speedwell whose dark blue flowers in loose racemes delight the eye all through summer. These brooks are probably the least polluted of all our waters; they are largely out of reach of sewage effluents, and as they pass through pasture-land rather than through arable, they receive the least amount of fertiliser run-off, though they may receive some, because even pasture these days gets its quota of nitro-chalk or sulphate of ammonia.

The plant has rather dark, fleshy leaves, elliptical and blunt, with very fine teeth. It is anchored by creeping rhizomes. The stem is fleshy and hollow. The underwater portions harbour nymphs and rarely cause silting. Even if the plant harboured no fly life it would still be an asset because of its beauty.

The Whorled Water Milfoil, *Myriophyllum verticillatum*, seems to have received less attention than its spiked cousin, yet both are in the highest class as supporters of algae and other organisms, and this is reflected in the excellent fauna they carry.

Both plants are similar in appearance, and both are submerged, except for the emergent flowers (see Spiked Water Milfoil for general description). The main differences are that the spiked species has leaves and flowers in whorls of four, while the other has leaves mainly in whorls of five, and flowers in whorls of six.

It may be that a flourishing periphyton is connected with the chemical composition of plants, because in the water milfoils we have two species that not only carry a rich periphyton, but are also rich in nutrients. When the leaves die they form valuable material for bacterial activity. The milfoils can be so profuse, especially in chalk streams, as to cause silting, and reduction of beds may be necessary in some circumstances, but I would certainly hesitate a long time before attempting any complete removal.

Among the pond plants we have several that possess good qualities, and one or two that can present problems. With most of them we must balance their value as oxygen producers against the fact that where they occur in masses they will shelter fish, but will also reduce the area over which flies can be cast. In some respects they may be regarded as plants that encourage skilful fishing, because it is often necessary to drop the fly very precisely in narrow channels between the beds, and if the fish takes, it is then necessary to play it very delicately to guide it out of the channels into open water. The same principle applies of course in streams where weed beds are prolific, and the great G. E. M. Skues postulated that a checked fish goes to weed, while an unchecked one flounders on the surface. In other words, if the angler's first reaction to the take is to tighten hard, the fish will respond by boring weedwards. It cannot then be checked without running the risk of a broken leader; thus all that can be done is to give it line, with the inevitable plunge into the weeds, where the fish may well be lost.

The Floating Crystalwort, *Riciella fluitans*, occurs in trout ponds, producing small, star-shaped rosettes of leaves, sometimes confused with the foliage of starwort. But it is a simple matter to distinguish the two, since starwort is rooted, while crystalwort floats and can be scooped off the surface. Occasionally a stem will be held in the mud, though not truly rooted, by a rhizoid. The plant spreads by elongation and a distinct forking. The stems are well charged with oxygen to give buoyancy, and the plant is an excellent oxygenator. Thus it is one to be valued, and its clearance is necessary only when dense beds occur. I do not know whether it is, in general, a good or a poor supporter of a periphyton, but I have not found more than a few odd nymphs, usually Pond Olives, among its foliage.

A floating plant that does carry a good fauna is Frogbit, *Hydrocharis morsus-ranae*. This has roundish, heart-shaped leaves just over 1½in in diameter, with clearly visible parallel veins following the general leaf shape, ie arcuate veins. The foliage forms a rosette. There are white flowers, occurring either singly or in twos or threes. The single ones are female, the doubles or triples usually male, but sometimes the flowers are of one sex only, and the plant does not rely on sexual reproduction but reproduces also by means of stolons, ie submerged stems carrying buds that give rise to new growth.

The under surfaces of frogbit leaves are well colonised by animals on which trout feed and are a particular haunt of snails. The plant can spread excessively, and some degree of eradication is often necessary.

The Duckweeds, *Lemna* spp, can be a fearful pest in small trout ponds. They are small floating plants whose leaves are technically known as thalli. Each thallus bears a root projecting into the water, or there may be several roots, or none, according to species.

Propagation is by means of budding, when new leaves grow from the edges of old ones; it can be very rapid and extensive, and the plants may spread over the water surface very quickly. The most common is *L. minor*, with mainly egg-shaped thalli about 3mm long, with one root. The thalli are mostly light green, but some occur that are darker green on the upper surface and lighter on the lower.

The Great Duckweed, *L. polyrrhiza*, has thalli about twice the size of those of the first species. They are usually green above and reddish below, and each has several roots in bundles.

The Gibbous Duckweed, *L. gibba*, is slightly larger than *L. minor* and is distinguished by having a swollen under surface. This species has one root per leaf.

The smallest of all is the Least Duckweed, which belongs to a different genus and is named *Wolffia arrhiza*. Its leaves are tiny, measuring about 1–1·5mm. They are slightly swollen on both surfaces, and do not bear roots.

These plants are characterised by having upper leaf surfaces that are just above the water surface, and so remain dry, but one species, Ivy Duckweed, *L. trisulca*, is submerged. Its leaves, or thalli, are quite distinct in shape, being lance-like, and grow out of one another on stalks. The description 'ivy' or 'ivy leaved' is not very precise, but it does give an idea of the roughly lobed pattern of the thalli. Each thallus normally has one root, and during winter these peculiar plants sink to the pond bed.

I think it may fairly be said that duckweeds are more of a curse than a blessing. They can spread so quickly and so thickly that sunlight penetration may be severely inhibited, with the result that better plants are prevented from growing, oxygenating processes are curtailed, and the water is made unsuitable for trout. The leaves are heavily charged with starch, which can hardly be good for trout, and rotting duckweed leaves produce an unsatisfactory form of detritus. Ducks, presumably, like duckweed, but, delightful creatures that they are, they are the last things we want in a trout pond.

A floating-leaved plant which deserves our praise is Amphibious Bistort, *Polygonum amphibium*. It is rooted in the pond bank or in the mud of shallow water by creeping rhizomes, and roots also grow from buds on the submerged stems. The floating stems are about 3ft long, and bear long-leaf stalks that carry roughly lance-shaped leaves but with a rather blunt point. They are held in the horizontal and are shiny, dark green and leathery. The veining is characteristic, consisting of a midrib from base to apex from which lateral veins are given off to form two clearly discernible parallel patterns, one on each side of the midrib, to give a generally herringbone effect. Flowering stems emerge to a height of 2–3in above water and bear pinkish flowers that are small, but concentrated in a tightly formed cylindrical inflorescence, which is quite conspicuous.

This is a lovely plant for trout waters. The leaves are large enough to provide a good surface area for a periphyton and the animals it supports, yet are arranged in the water in such a manner that there is plenty of space between them for sunlight to penetrate. Furthermore it has the great virtue of being able to survive over winter in the damp mud of drained ponds, and soon re-establishes when the pond bed is re-filled.

One of the most welcome mosses is the Willow Moss, *Fontinalis antipyretica*, which occurs in lakes and streams. It has stems of about 24in tightly clothed in small, lance-shaped leaflets held so closely all the way up the stems that no stem can be seen, and the large floating tufts of stems look like thin, green ropes, and not at all what one would expect a moss to look like. Nevertheless, it is technically a moss.

Willow moss is a good harbourer of aquatic fauna. It does not cause silting-up, since the stems are resilient to the current and are spaced widely enough to allow an unimpeded flow.

I have left to the last two plants that every angler must surely recognise, namely the White Water Lily, *Nymphaea alba*, and the Yellow Water Lily, or Brandy Bottle, *Nuphar lutea*. These can need no description, but they do need to be considered. Both are very beautiful plants which no man, angler or not, would wish to destroy. However, they possess thick rhizomes that can reach 3 yd in length and will produce new shoots, and the root area can become a maze of growth, overtopped by a dense leaf cover that may spread over large areas of water.

These plants must, therefore, be kept within bounds in trout waters.

CHAPTER 9

The Periphyton

WE HAVE seen several references to the periphyton and brief indications of its composition. Since it is the food layer on which plant-supported animals depend for their existence, its presence is obviously essential to the fly-fisher's fauna, so we should spend a few minutes considering it. To spend a few minutes considering one of the most complex life patterns in the aquatic environment is like 'doing' the Sistine Chapel, or the Louvre, or the British Museum in typical tourist fashion, but we must either consider the subject briefly, or not at all, or else in great detail. Detailed consideration is far beyond the scope of this book; to ignore the subject would be to imply that it is unimportant. We will therefore take the middle way.

Freshwater contains vast quantities of free-floating plants and animals which are known collectively as plankton. The animals are called animal plankton, or zooplankton, the plants phytoplankton. They occupy the illuminated areas of water. Although the plants are primitive, they share the photosynthetic processes of higher plants, and they return organic nutrients of a fundamental nature to the water.

Phytoplankton assumes a multiplicity of shapes and sizes, from the microscopic one-celled plant called *Chlamydomonas*, to the giant seaweed, *Macrocystis*, which may reach several hundreds of feet in length. The former occurs visibly as a green scum on the surface of standing water; it is obviously not microscopic in the mass, but the mass is the total of many millions of plants.

The unicellular plant is the lowest form of plant life, yet it is a microcosm, complete in itself, and containing chlorophyll. For example, *Chlamydomonas* is a roughly egg-shaped cell made up of a cellulose wall enclosing a chloroplast which contains cytoplasm surrounding a cell nucleus. There is a protein substance in a small egg-shaped container against the outside of the chloroplast wall, and there are starch grains between the cell wall and the chloroplast wall. There is also an 'eye spot' which is thought to be sensitive to the direction of light, and coming from the cytoplasm is a pair of long thread-like flagella, which constantly vibrate and provide the plant's motion. It is a motile plant and moves from place to place of its own volition.

A higher stage of algal development occurs in plants whose cells divide, to give further divisions leading to a chain of cells. Again, filamentous algae may thicken and expand to form thalli, and may assume a superficial appearance of higher plants. But the functions of the tissues are limited to the building up of conduction cells and the utilising of chlorophyll. Another difference between higher plants and algae is that some algae do not contain starch, but contain instead a specialised product called laminarin. Colouring matter other than chlorophyll may be present, giving the algae a brown or a red appearance, but the chlorophyll is always there and is merely masked by the other substances. These can be dissolved by placing the algae in hot water, when the green colour of the chlorophyll will be clearly seen.

Unlike higher plants, which absorb soluble salts through their root hairs and carbon through their leaves, algae absorb over their entire surface. If we brush our hands over a mass of algae we see many bubbles breaking in the water. This is the result of oxygen reaching the surface, and which has been liberated into the water from the algal cells.

Reproduction methods in algae are almost as varied as the plants themselves. Some green types reproduce through a single sex spore; when the protoplasm leaves the cell, it sprouts minute hair-like growths called cilia, and by their aid swims around for a short period before settling down to its own life as a new plant. This type of spore is known as a Zoospore.

G

Another method is conjugated reproduction, when two cells, seemingly of no distinction in sex, merge together in the water to give a single spore known as a Zygospore, which attaches itself to a plant or a stone and develops into a filamentous alga. The higher in the evolutionary scale the algal species are, the more complicated, or the more advanced, do the reproduction processes become.

The forms most familiar to anglers are the green and the blue-green, which are also among the simplest. The chlorophyll of the blue-green is frequently obscured by bluish, reddish or brownish pigments. Some of these types being very primitive, have no cell nucleus but reproduce by fission. Cell shapes are greatly varied, according to algal species. Some are spherical; others egg-shaped, others again S-shaped. In some species the cells are joined by filaments; in others they are enclosed within a gelatinous substance.

Most of the blue-green algae are non-motile, and progression about the water surface is dictated by the movement of the water under stress of wind, but some types do undulate, though still remaining in the same position on the water surface.

Many green algae are more advanced than the blue-green. Their pigment is pure green, and their structure and reproduction processes are relatively complex; but simple, single-celled types also exist. In the mass, these algae are present in the wads that present the appearance of a large floating type of 'scummy' plant. Some are distinctly soft and slimy to the touch; others are firmer. In general, two main groups are represented, according to whether the algae are slimy or firm. The former belong primarily to *Spirogyra*; the latter to *Cladophora*.

Other forms of microscopic or exceedingly small plants are the Diatoms. These are brown and are covered by silica, and therefore may be considered as hard-shelled. A diatom has one cell with a nucleus, and reproduction is by fission, when the cell divides and each half produces a smaller half. This process continues, with the newly produced half-cells getting smaller each time, until finally a different method of reproduction, by means of spores, takes over.

Yet another group is the Flagellates, which are motile and move freely in the water by means of thread-like flagella. These are unicellular and possess a nucleus, though some types are less advanced than others. The least advanced comprise a simple cell with an outer covering, while in the higher forms the cell is surrounded by cellulose and the internal composition is more evolved.

Seen from a pond or river bank, or when removed in disgust from a fish hook, algae appear as nothing more than green or brown slime. But seen under a microscope, they take on an incredibly different appearance. Some are delicately formed in precise geometrical patterns; others resemble necklaces, chains, or wheel spokes; others again are like star-shaped petals or leaves. Many of these forms cannot be fully appreciated with a magnification of less than 150, which gives some idea of their minute size.

There are, of course, algae which are not directly associated with plants; some float for a time, then sink to the bottom; some swim; some attach themselves to stones on the river bed. Those which form a plant periphyton are largely confined to the green and blue-green species and the diatoms having special attachment stalks, or pads, with which they anchor themselves to plant surfaces. Here, again, a plant periphyton is an apparently uninteresting coating of slime, but if we place a length of stem, or a leaf, under the microscope, we shall see an extraordinary collection of growths of all shapes and sizes that at first sight seems like one of those crazy artistic concoctions that are deemed works of genius by trendy intellectuals, instead of being dismissed for the nonsense that they are. But if we look more closely (not at the artistic concoctions, but at the periphyton, which is infinitely more worthy of attention) we shall discern a most marvellous pattern of order within what first appeared to be meaningless confusion. We shall see perhaps a dozen different types of algae, all beautifully formed, some strangely formed, some simple, some elaborate, and ever after the slime on a water milfoil leaf will take on a new and utterly fascinating character.

The periphyton is not composed entirely of phytoplankton, but includes members of the zooplankton. Prominent among these are the single-celled organisms known as Protozoa. There are also various forms of bacteria on which animals grazing the periphyton are presumed to feed.

Although I have already mentioned that the presence of green and blue-green algae is a sign of flourishing water, there are certain reservations we must note. One green alga, *Cladophora glomerata* is associated with sewage effluent. It does not appear to thrive in water that is heavily polluted with this, but rather in the zone where the sewage had undergone some stage of decomposition. Its presence can be a good indicator of what might be termed second-degree sewage pollution, and it may occur a long way below the source of the pollution and may come to rest in shallow water. Where this alga is identified, its presence could therefore point to sewage pollution somewhere upstream, though not necessarily, since it is not confined to polluted or semi-polluted water.

Gross pollution by sewage effluent is in a different category. The hideous, evil-smelling deposits are loosely referred to as sewage fungus, and some types of fungi are probably present, also some types of algae, but the basis of the deposits is primarily bacterial rather than fungal, and the latter are more in the nature of secondary matter.

Mild pollution associated with *C. glomerata* is not necessarily detrimental to trout waters. In fact it is a type of enrichment which may lead to the growth of rooted plants to which a periphyton becomes attached, and there are records of good trout growth in such circumstances. But much depends on the flow, the types of plants and their oxygenating properties, and the ability of the water to clear out potentially dangerous accumulations of nutrient salts. A chain of events deleterious to fish life can occur. If the flow is too slow, and particularly if the water is shallow, the effluent remains largely static. Sunlight will penetrate the shallow water sufficiently to encourage a dense growth of algae which will use up oxygen beyond the limit tolerated by trout and the fauna feeding on the periphyton, and a condition akin to induced pollution will arise.

Where the stream takes other alien substances, these will soon contribute to the pollution, and a disastrous situation may arise. Bore-hole extraction, if it seriously reduces the volume of water flowing down, will be a direct factor in aggravating the pollution, sometimes to the point where the stream, or certain parts of it where effluent has built up, will no longer support trout, and may no longer support any animals other than the relatively few pollution-tolerant species.

It has been said that there is occasionally some confusion in the minds of anglers over what constitutes 'pure' water. Thus the gin-clear pool, devoid of plants and algae, and with a bed of glittering gravel—water 'that you could drink'—is sometimes taken as the criterion. No doubt it is pure in the popular sense, but beautiful though it is to look at, and however welcome as liquid to assuage thirst and cool a parched throat, it is in fishing terms more or less sterile. Conversely, water that is liberally populated by plants, or at any rate in which algae are seen, is thought to be polluted in some degree.

The best way to correct these misapprehensions is to consider the chalk stream. It is water of the clearest kind, and if clarity is regarded as a sign of purity, we can say it is water of the purest kind. Yet it contains innumerable plants and the algae that form on these. In fishing terms, its purity is not necessarily related to its clarity, but more to its high oxygen content, which is a direct result of its plants.

The rivers Wye and Severn are, at the present time, among the purest in the country throughout much of their lengths, yet they are by no means gin-clear everywhere and at all times. In some reaches, and at some periods, they are quite the reverse, especially after heavy rain in the up-river areas.

It cannot be stressed too strongly that trout waters do not *have* to be gin-clear to be pure, but they must have plant communities, and very often the plants, by retarding in some measure the flowing away of silt, contribute to the lack of clarity which is mistakenly seen as evidence of lack of purity.

I think these points deserve mention, because I have known anglers to condemn waters as polluted merely because 'blanket weed' was present, when in fact chemical analysis showed that no pollution was evident, or that if it was, it was expressed simply in a temporary lowering of oxygen due to immediate climatic factors, and was not a permanent feature.

A contrast in trout waters is provided by the mountain brooks and the moorland streams. Both are normally pure, and the former are normally as clear as chalk streams, while the latter are frequently brownish in colour. The mountain brooks do not contain many higher plants, but their stones and rocks are heavily coated with mosses and algae, which in darker waters are sometimes erroneously taken as signs of impurity. Here again the clarity of the water is not necessarily the yardstick of purity, but is due to the fact that very little suspended matter is present.

Even where suspended matter is present, as in the peaty streams of moorlands, it is not a sign of pollution in these streams. In fact, nutritionally, peat is virtually an inert substance and does not contribute to the chemical over-enrichment that is the basis of pollution.

It really comes down to what I have said before, namely that pollution in the modern meaning is almost solely caused by man, and very seldom by nature. Pollution in the sense of lowered oxygen and excessive carbon dioxide does certainly occur from time to time in nature, but it is nearly always a temporary factor. In any case, although it is often regarded as pollution in the modern sense, this attitude is far from being correct, since temporary shortages of oxygen occurring in water through natural agencies are quite unrelated to the gross chemical pollution caused by man.

CHAPTER 10

Weed Cutting

TO SAY that weed cutting is often done without consideration of the effects on animal life may seem a bold assertion, but I think it is justified. The statement does not reflect on the intelligence of those who do the cutting, or are responsible for its ordering. It is simply that riparian owners and weed-cutting contractors, and even many anglers, are not always particularly knowledgeable about what goes on in a weed bed. The primary object of the water authorities is to prevent flooding, and some of them tend to see weed beds not as vital components of a trout fishery, but rather as the agents of flood waters. Some riparian owners put their faith and trust in the authorities to a degree that is somewhat alarming, when we consider that, to a considerable extent, the interests of the two are directly opposed. Authority wants to shave the weeds down to a crew-cut; ownership is, or should be, concerned with conserving them to the maximum consistent with authority's legitimate needs.

Let us first consider the river that arises from springs that have only a moderate summer output. In winter, when the springs are fully charged and when most of the river weeds have died down, the flow will be strong, the volume relatively large, and the level will be well up. The impression may then be gained that the water-course is one that carries a large volume of water not merely in winter, but in summer as well. Such an impression would be illusory, and would be shown to be so to anyone who kept careful records of water levels, if weeds were crew-cut in summer, because immediately after the cutting the level would drop perceptibly. It would then be evident that the summer water level, before severe weed cutting, was being maintained not by the springs, but by the weeds.

We sometimes have in chalk streams (where perhaps 90 per cent of all weed cutting is done) two basically different sets of conditions. One is the river where a high summer output from the springs combines with weed growth to give bank flooding, if weed cutting is inadequate; the other is a low output from the springs which can be compensated for only by minimal weed cutting.

One unfortunate aspect of heavy weed cutting in early spring in the low-volume river is that the water that has built up over winter is released at a speed which is excessive for trout. It suits the river authority man perfectly; he dreads, and rightly so, the prospect of floods, and he loves to see the freed water rushing merrily along to the sea, or the Thames, or wherever it goes. But it is a very different story for the man who is putting hundreds of pounds worth of trout in the water, and who is labouring under the happy misapprehension that those expensive fish will string out and take up stations all along his beat. If the beats are divided up and allocated to anglers, who may be paying anything up to £300 for a season's rod, those unfortunate enough to find themselves in the beat highest upstream, where the full force of the released water will be greatest, will not catch many fish, because there will not be many there. As the season advances the river will settle down to a more moderate flow, but valuable fishing time will have been lost.

There is usually a compromise solution to most seemingly intractable problems, and the one here is not only to cut lightly, but to cut in channels, instead of right across the weed mass. It is far preferable to make fewer cuts in strategic places to channel the water, than to go at it baldheaded, removing the whole lot.

The latter method is usually preferred by the river authorities, first because being unselective, it makes no demands on men who, adept enough at the physical work, cannot be expected to be surveyors interested in the wiles of water, and second because it is more appropriate to any bonus system of payment, where the operators are paid a bonus on completing a given area. If the bonus applies to a hundred-yard stretch, then all the weeds in that stretch must be cut.

However, water being water, there is really no exact rule that will apply everywhere, and in rivers fed by strong springs the summer levels may well demand harder weed cutting, but even here the channelling method applies. It is simply a case of cutting more channels, and perhaps wider ones. The beds not within the channelled areas can often be lightly cut, or sometimes not cut at all.

It is time we now left this subject and got on to the main one of this chapter, which is the effect of cutting on the weed-bed fauna. We have already remarked on the disposition of such creatures as reed smut larvae, nymphs and shrimps along the fronds or at the base of crowfoot, and it is pertinent to take this plant as an example of the results of excessive weed cutting.

The populations of reed smut larvae will be building up along the growing fronds from the time these start elongating. By early April most larvae will have left the frond bases in favour of the better washed apical portions, and there may be basal lengths of perhaps 12–15in that are almost devoid of larvae. If the beds are cut hard in early April, leaving only about 6in of growth, the population will be drastically reduced, perhaps even destroyed, and a reduced one will remain at a low level.

This could mean that instead of there being a peak fly emergence in early summer, as is normally the case in the natural course of events, there would be a greatly diminished one. This condition would be much aggravated by the traditional July cut being a hard one; as a result, the September peak, again a normal occurrence in nature, would likewise be severely reduced.

Since there is 'staggered' development of larvae within a colony according to individual stages of growth, it may seem reasonable to conclude that perhaps quite appreciable numbers carried down on cut weed will be at the pupal stage and will later emerge successfully as flies, to provide a nucleus of a later generation.

However, this conclusion is not as comforting as it may sound, because the main emergence stage of the summer flies is sometime in June, and if the beds are cut hard in April, none of the larvae on the floating weed will be anywhere near the comparatively safe pupal stage. The mortality rate of the immature larvae is almost impossible to assess, but let us consider the perils that beset them on floating weed.

The mechanism by which the larvae trap and filter their food, ie the filtering plumes, is intimately adapted to the position of the plants, and to the flow of the water. The larvae must assume a posture in which their plumes are kept in constant motion by the current, which means that the body, anchored by the suction pad, is projected more or less at right angles to the supporting plant base. If the plumes were held head-on to the current they would be washed back on themselves and kept in that position, when food would flow over the creature's head and away downstream. If the plumes were held downstream they would be equally useless, and would resemble an umbrella blown inside out by a gust of wind. Thus the position on the plant assumed by the larvae is vital to their existence.

Now when cut weed is floating downstream, the larvae it is carrying are suddenly faced with quite different conditions. They are still anchored to the drifting weed, but the anchorage is no longer stable. The weed may change course, become swirled round in eddies, drift into calm or static water, with the result that the equilibrium of the larvae suffers great upset, and their filtering plumes may be subjected to conditions that cause their collapse or their actual destruction.

Although it is impossible to assess exactly the impact on population levels of hard cutting, what can hardly be gainsaid is that if large numbers of immature larvae are cut adrift from their moorings and sent downstream to combat conditions that are altogether at variance with those under which they normally develop, then a severe upset to their life cycle is inevitable.

The same goes for nymphs. Those which are strong swimmers and have reached a stage where they can withstand a normal degree of buffeting by the water may at least be able to swim far enough to find another weed bed, but that will not help then much if all the beds are being shaved. And as the principle is to work upstream when cutting, to prevent cut weed from being held up, it is obvious that there will be few havens left in the beat being cut.

In practice, nymphs are much less at risk than reed smut larvae, since many can remain on the floating weed without their feeding habits being dislocated, and will reach the fly stage unharmed. But they may well hatch in the beat of the man downstream, and the water where the weeds were cut will be largely flyless. The fact remains, however, that not all species are adapted to this unnatural transport, and I doubt whether anyone knows exactly what the effects are likely to be on, for example, a Blue-winged Olive nymph, which prefers calm conditions, when it finds its peaceful little home deep in ranunculus fronds suddenly washed away into rough water.

Shrimps must have a particularly rough time when they are set adrift in strong currents. They cannot swim far, and unless they can soon find a safe harbourage they will not stand much chance of survival.

At first sight, shrimps may be thought to be at minimum risk from hard cutting, since they largely occupy the quieter and more silted areas deep in the plant bed. But these stations are made suitable by the plant itself. Its fronds expand and cover a widening area, thus deflecting the current so that this, instead of washing vigorously over the bed, becomes forked and glides round the edges of the bed. This leads to the accumulations of silt that suit the shrimps. But when the bed is crew-cut the current is no longer forked; it rushes over the shorn weed, dispersing silt and shrimps, and the latter are simply washed away.

Excessive weed cutting is far from universal, and I do not want this chapter to be taken as any inference to the contrary. There are a great many stretches where excellent programmes are evident, but we cannot ignore the fact that the reverse also applies elsewhere. Mechanisation is, of course, partly to blame. Powered cutters will slice off a bed in a fraction of the time taken by manual ones. They cannot select for height as they proceed. The craft chugs along, or sometimes goes at nearly speedboat pace, and the cutters leave a trail of devastation in their wake. A leading fishing journal once illustrated an article of mine with a picture of just such an operation, and captioned it 'Midsummer Madness'. Perhaps that should have been the title of this chapter.

CHAPTER 11

Chemical Control

WE NOW enter what might well become in the very near future the most controversial of all trout-fishing matters. It is controversial already, but only to a somewhat mild extent, as chemical weed control has not yet fully burst upon the fishing scene.

First of all we have to distinguish between two fundamental principles in relation to manual as opposed to chemical control. The first, sensibly carried out, seeks to reduce top growth; the second seeks to kill it. That is a bald statement, and open to argument as far as chemicals are concerned, for several have only a partial effect. But there are some chemicals that kill top growth outright, not always of all species, but of some, and a perusal of manufacturers' literature will make it evident that the property of a once-for-all kill for the season from one application is regarded as a virtue.

Cut weed normally regenerates quite quickly, and even where cutting is excessive, little if any damage is done as far as the weeds are concerned. Furthermore, the cut material can be drifted down to a catchment pond, pulled out and used for compost. Not all trout fisheries possess catchment ponds, but those designed by far-seeing owners do. Weed cutting done properly and at periods when there will be the least interference with the life cycles of the fauna, has been going on successfully for generations. The fact that such cutting fits in with the life cycles may to some extent be fortuitous, but is none the less a fact.

Thus weeds lightly cut in April will inevitably disturb some life cycles, but not sufficiently to diminish fly life severely. A further cut in July fits in with the 'dog days', when trout fishing is more or less dead, and is also done when the major hatch of the first part of the season has ended. By the time the weeds have re-grown, they will coincide with the egg-laying and nymph-feeding periods that are the basis of the life cycles for the second part of the season, when we get the autumn broods of olives, reed smut larvae and so on.

Thus there is a clearly discernible pattern of co-existence between the weeds and the animals. Nothing, or very little, is killed; life goes on. We have merely checked the weeds, and by so doing have ensured their regeneration.

When we embark on killing methods we are immediately interfering drastically with that long established pattern. Again, we need take only one weed to illustrate the point, so let us take crowfoot, which is completely susceptible to certain herbicides, and whose top growth is killed outright by these for the entire season.

There are basically two methods of application. One is the very early post-emergent, when the material is applied at the stage where the new season's growth has just started. The other is the late post-emergent, when the material is applied to established growths. The term 'applied to growths' need not necessarily be taken literally, because some materials are in granular form, and the granules are applied to the water surface, when they sink to the mud to release their active ingredients, which are translocated to the plant foliage via the roots. We are, in any case, concerned not with the practical treatments, but with the principles of herbicidal control.

The arguments for early post-emergent treatment are that weeds are killed before they have had a chance to arrest or disorganise water flow and cause silting-up, and that by killing the foliage in the very young stage we are not left with heavy stands of rotting vegetation that would cause de-nitrification. Here it should be understood that chemically-killed foliage does not generally break away and get carried downstream; it remains to rot *in situ*.

My argument against early post-emergent treatment is that by killing the young crowfoot fronds it kills the creatures that live on those fronds. Death is indirect, because all materials passed by the Pesticides Safety Precaution Scheme—and no one but a raving lunatic would use any others—are non-toxic to fish and other aquatic fauna. But death is death, no matter how it comes. Remove the crowfoot fronds, and you remove the means of life of the creatures these support. Furthermore, you do so far more effectively than by cutting. The cut beds do regenerate, and quickly; the chemically-treated ones do not.

The argument in favour of late post-emergent treatment, if there is one, and this is a point on which I am admittedly hazy, must be that it is done when the fly life has matured and the hatch completed. Against it we have stands of rotting weeds that will inevitably have adverse effects because of the de-nitrification that will ensue. In the *Code Of Practice For The Use Of Herbicides On Weeds In Watercourses And Lakes*, the Ministry of Agriculture recommends that no more than a quarter of a lake area, and no more than quarter-mile stretches of narrow watercourses, should be treated at one time, and that treated stretches of streams should be separated by untreated stretches of similar lengths. The reason is that if treated areas become too low in oxygen, fish will move to untreated ones.

This is fine in theory, but what are the results in practice? Trout dislike communal living; their first instinct on being introduced to streams from stewponds is to find their own private quarters. If they are herded into short stretches of water in numbers larger than these would naturally accommodate, they are liable to suffer competition for food, and anglers will be liable to competition for trout, if the number of anglers who would normally fish a half-mile beat have to be concentrated over a quarter mile.

The questions of chemical selectivity and degree of weed death need considering. It is feasible in theory to omit weed species, or beds of particular species, that are susceptible to a chemical if the weeds are considered desirable, and to treat only less desirable ones; or if they are all desirable to treat only limited areas. But faunas may be abundant on one bed and sparse on another. Without carefully inspecting the beds before treatment, even supposing he knew what to look for and how to assess populations, the operator might well eliminate a thriving population while leaving a scanty one.

Some chemicals have only partial effects, and this leads their exponents to assume that the amount of weed surviving would compensate in terms of animal life for the amount killed. But the weeds that are killed by one representative type of herbicide include starwort, whirled water milfoil, frogbit and crowfoot, all of which are good supporters of trout food, while those that resist it, either completely or partly, comprise mainly reeds, rushes and similar emergents along stream banks, together with one or two of greater value like shining pondweed and amphibious bistort.

Even supposing the last two were in close association with milfoil and crowfoot, which may not be very likely, their survival, or partial survival, with that of the animals they carried, might not compensate for the loss of the populations on crowfoot and milfoil.

I do not want to give the impression that herbicides are passed for use willy nilly. On the contrary, they have to undergo the most stringent tests before they can be approved under the official safety scheme, and their makers must satisfy the ministry that the chemicals do not present hazards to fish and aquatic fauna in general. For example, some seventy species of mites, larvae, worms, snails, leeches and beetles were involved in the testing of one chemical, together with many different species of fish in all stages from egg to adult fish, and phytoplankton were also included. The tests were carried out in many parts of the world.

It is not, as I indicated earlier, the problem of direct toxicity that is in question; what is in question is the effect of plant death in trout-fishing waters where nymph and dry fly are the primary or exclusive methods.

The general facts given above centre round the seventy species that emerged unscathed from herbicide trials, and any fly-fishing reader who has manfully struggled thus far through this book will immediately spot the fact that of the animals mentioned only those grouped as larvae would interest him, and then only if they were larvae of anglers' flies.

In other words, if we take this example as representing the approach in general, which is probably a fair assumption, we cannot escape the suspicion that dry-fly fishing has been given something less than the attention it deserves. It would appear that there has been inadequate recognition of the narrow limits within which the dry-fly angler works, or that the plants of his waters are absolutely essential to his mode of fishing.

It is no good assuring a dry-fly man that his stream will still be crawling with worms and leeches after the weeds have been killed off. These creatures, good as they are in their own right, are not of the slightest use to him. He wants his crowfoot and celery and the rest, with their fly-fishing populations.

Are we then reduced to the choice of either early post-emergent treatments that will leave the treated areas of our stream plantless and flyless, or to late post-emergent ones that will leave us with masses of rotting vegetation, de-nitrified water, and trout whose equilibrium has been rudely shattered?

There is never any guarantee that fly life will be at a high level in any given year. It is subject to natural fluctuations at the best of times, and although steady average populations may be maintained over a period, there are some seasons when the figures are well below the average, just as there are others when they are well above.

We cannot afford to do anything that might reduce the low figures, and we should realise that however good we imagine the average to be, it is really appreciably lower in some areas than it used to be, or numbers of certain species are lower. The true

H

mayflies (Figs 26 and 27), which of course are not plant-supported species, are an example; these have steadily declined on some waters over the past thirty years or so, though we cannot say with certainty that the decline is due to man's interference for they started to vanish from the middle Itchen long before technology really got into its terrifying stride.

The point is that to indulge in any weed control method which is obviously going to diminish fly populations could be utter stupidity. It may be that I am exaggerating the peril. At the moment there is no proof one way or the other, but neither was there any proof that certain insecticides used in horticulture in the early 1950s would wipe out invaluable predators, and thus create a pest position infinitely worse than obtained before the insecticides were used. Yet they did create exactly that problem.

In the aquatic field, the problems are greater than in the terrestrial, because the life forms of the former are confined to a limited environment, either throughout all their stages of development or through-

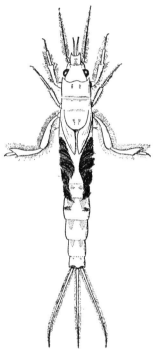

FIG 26 Nymph of Mayfly, *Ephemera danica*, 24mm long, from life

out the larger part of these. They cannot escape man's depredations to the extent that wholly terrestrial forms can. It would be difficult to pollute a whole countryside with chemicals, but easy to pollute the whole, or most, of a small trout stream.

In fact we may think that assurances of non-toxicity of weed control chemicals in fishing waters are somewhat premature. Vast numbers of microscopic organisms are involved, apart from the comparatively large creatures and the fish. Nobody knows what the effects of aquatic herbicides may be on the infinitesimal occupants of freshwaters, or the results that might stem from harming these. They are not mere flotsam; they are part of the aquatic environment and fulfil the purposes for which nature designed them. Some are predators, others parasites; all are part of the immense complexity of water life.

In the light of current work on the subject the position seems to be that aquatic herbicides are acceptable in coarse-fishing waters and that, within certain limits, they are acceptable in trout waters

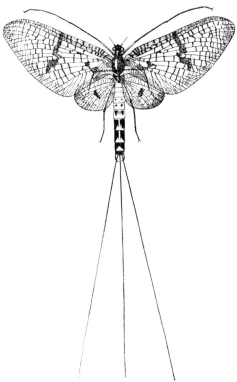

Fig 27 Male imago (spinner) of Mayfly,
Ephemera danica × 3·25

where wet fly is the standard method. The limiting factor in the
latter is that many anglers include nymph representations among
the wet flies. They use either specific nymph patterns, such as
Lake and Pond Olives, or nymph-like ones like Williams Favourite
fished wet, and the various 'spider' and copper wire types, eg the
lightly hackled Snipe series and the Pheasant Tail respectively. It
is not much good using these if trout are not feeding on nymphs,
and they will not if the nymph-bearing plants have been destroyed.

Certain herbicides tend to diffuse in still waters, and the possibility arises that beds which were not intended for treatment but
which were near the treated ones might receive diffused chemical.
Perhaps the greatest problem in treating still waters is to select the
beds. They are much more difficult to locate in any sizeable area of
water than they are in chalk streams, and their positions and con-
stitution cannot be accurately determined without a careful
survey.

Thus without plotting their positions, the policy of treating no
more than a quarter of a lake area at a time could be something of
a hit-and-run one. It could be that the treated area contained the
richest food-bearing plants, or were essential oxygenators, as in
the case I mentioned earlier, where all the visibly feeding trout
concentrated in the pondweed zone. Indeed, that particular pond
provided a perfect example of how easy it would be to regard a
weedy area as being a candidate for chemicals, and of how disastrous chemical treatment could prove to be. Where a weed species
was fulfilling an indispensable function in oxygenating the water,
its destruction would not only nullify the function but would
completely reverse it, because instead of providing oxygen as
living plants, the pondweeds would, in their decomposing state,
become a direct cause of diminished oxygen. On such a day as the
one I described, when trout were obviously concentrated in the
pondweed zone because of the oxygen that was available there,
they would be in the greatest distress if such an area were denied
them.

Summing up, I would say that the time has not yet come for

aquatic herbicides in nymph and dry-fly waters. That is not my opinion only; it is shared by people whose knowledge of fresh-water biology is vastly greater than mine. At least one biologist of international repute has sounded a warning note. It is a note that should be heeded.

CHAPTER 12

Planting Weeds: Use of Groins

THE PRIMARY object of planting weeds in chalk streams is to diversify a too strong flow. The type of water in which weed planting is likely to be most necessary is the narrow, swiftly flowing stream, rather than the large river. It is also likely to be most successful in the former. Feeder streams, particularly if they rise at some considerable distance from the fishery, may run too fast for trout in the lower reaches, in which case the fish will use them mainly for spawning, and will run up to the headwaters in late autumn for that purpose, always assuming that the main river carries wild specimens.

It is not uncommon to find feeders on a chalk-stream fishery which contain few trout, but which could be turned into first-rate waters if measures were taken to make the conditions more suitable. Usually, some stretches are suitable, and it is in these that any trout inhabiting the water will be seen, but there may be considerable lengths where the flow is excessive and where no fish reside.

It is sometimes thought that such streams are too narrow for good-sized fish, and that is perhaps the reason why no efforts are made to improve matters. This idea is quite wrong; it has been advanced with the narrow, rocky streams of the uplands in mind, or the narrow moorland streams, both of which carry only small trout.

But the two types of water are totally dissimilar, and bear no comparison as trout environments. Every fly fisher who delights in the well vegetated side streams of the chalk country knows that these harbour very fine trout, sometimes of 2lb and often in the 1 to 1½lb range.

But it will frequently be observed that where the water is too fast the swift flow will extend from bank to bank, and there will be no sheltered bank lies or pools for the trout, and of course no hatches of plant-supported flies.

Enough has been said in the preceding pages to suggest that if we want to slow down the flow of a fast stream we must plant a fast-water species. It is hardly worth repeating, but I do so because I once visited someone who was trying to achieve the purpose with starwort, and it is possible that others have done the same.

Crowfoot is almost certainly the best plant for slowing down fast water, but it must be the right species. *R. aquatilis* is not principally a plant of fast water, but prefers a gentle current or no current at all. *R. circinatus* would be quite unsuitable for the same reason. Apart from its suitability for fast water, the species must, or should preferably be, one with floating leaves, since those with only submerged leaves do not divert the current to the same extent. Very often we find that a species with no floating leaves has enough diversionary effect to enable some silt to accumulate at the basal end of the plant, and this can be followed by the establishment of starwort in this region, when it will be the latter, rather than the crowfoot, that is diverting the flow, and the diversion can be so slight as to make little or no significant difference to the water that flows over the bed. Our main object in diverting the current is to provide relatively calm water immediately downstream of the plant, in which trout will lie and feed.

The two best species in my experience are *R. pseudofluitans* and *R. peltatus*. The method is to pull out portions of weed complete with good stem lengths carrying several nodes and to insert them into sacks filled with material from the stream bed. The open ends of the sacks should be firmly tied, and slits made in the upper surfaces, through which the plants are inserted. It is advisable to stitch the splits together after the plants have been set, leaving the heads free but the basal portions secure, to prevent the plants from being washed out before they have rooted.

I mentioned earlier an example of bad siting, which led to

excessive silting-up. Planting in mid-stream, as happened in that case, is all right provided the beds do not spread too far across the currents, and is often necessary if one is to divert the flow into the bank with the object of creating pools. In fact, this object is more generally achieved by using groins, but in plantless stretches weed beds are better since they fulfil purposes other than deflecting the current.

Planting should follow a definite pattern, and in order to achieve this it is necessary to visualise the likely effects on the current. The first principle is division of the current. It must meet an obstruction which causes it to fork. Immediately downstream of the fork and in the lee of the bed, there will be an area of comparative calm, in which trout will lie. The next step is to ensure that the checking of the current does not lead to an extra gathering of water along the paths pursued by the split currents. If these are not also checked they will gather momentum at only a short distance below the bed, and will also meet after being deflected from the bank, to provide a combined force. Also, if their impact is too strong on the banks they will cause erosion.

Thus we must plant further beds at strategic spots, which will not only progressively lessen the water force, but will also provide additional trout lies. My sketch plan (Fig 28), not drawn to scale, will, I hope, give some idea of the general principle. The length of water shown could be a hundred yards. The plants are concentrated mainly in the upstream portion of the stretch, where the current diversions and slacker water have combined to create conditions suitable for trout. Further downstream where the force of the broken current is diminished, fewer plants are set.

It will be seen that the effect of planting on this plan is not only to divert the main current, but to create secondary currents that follow approximately the path which the main current was taking before the weeds were planted. Along the planted stretch there is now no strong main current; this has been turned into a succession of diversions, so that at no point is its force as great as it was. The effect of each bed has been to create a three-pronged fork; two relatively swift currents glide round the bed, one on each side, and a middle and slower one glides over the bed, to form a trout lie in its lee. The rate of this flow will be acceptable to trout, and to the animals which will colonise the weed. Blue-winged Olive nymphs, in particular, will find ideal grazing territory; these, as we have seen, are dwellers on the margins of currents, and wherever the current divides and glides round the crowfoot beds the conditions will suit the nymphs.

WEED PLANTING IN A
FAST FEEDER STREAM

DIVISIONS OF CURRENT CAUSED.
BY ESTABLISHED BEDS

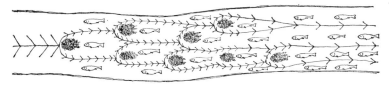

MAIN   CURRENT

FAST SECONDARY CURRENTS

PLANTS

FEEDING   AREAS FOR TROUT

FAST SECONDARY CURRENTS GRADUALLY DIMINISHING

FIG 28   Weed planting in fast water

Within the beds some silting-up will occur; immediately up-stream of them silt may accumulate too heavily, and attention to this possibility would be necessary. Where appropriate, the mud scoop would be used to remove excessive silt. The amount settling among the beds should not be too great; it would provide the right living conditions for shrimps, and would in any case be thinned out during winter by the flow, once the top growth had died down.

I

I must repeat what was said earlier about the changing nature of a stream. A single planting operation cannot be expected to provide a permanent solution to the problem of fast water. When we plant we are making alterations, which should be for the better, but the effects which we bring about rarely last for long. For example a bed, or several beds, might increase rapidly to cover a greater area than we had visualised; we might find silt accumulating where we had not expected it; a bank scour which at first looked excellent might become the source of insidious erosion. These are some of the possibilities we must always be prepared to consider.

Weed planting is not restricted to chalk streams. In our lowland Minnow Reach waters it may be just as desirable, though the primary reason will often be to speed up rather than slow down the water, while at the same time to provide breeding and grazing grounds for the plant fauna. In these waters it is chiefly a question of establishing small areas of faster water. In the main we cannot create long, relatively fast stretches without using groins, boulder dams and the like, though of course these can be erected as complementary measures to planting.

In slow waters we again use the principle of divided currents, for there is always a current of some kind, but we do not seek to diminish it downstream of the beds by further planting specifically to establish a series of split currents of lessening force. Instead, we allow the forked currents to gather what speed they can, and then plant more beds at their tails, to start another glide or pair of glides (Fig 29). This means that, length for length, we plant many more beds in the slow than in the fast stream, the object being to establish a series of short, swift glides, interspersed with equally short lengths of quieter water.

We again have slack water in the lee of the beds, but we have fast glides, eddies and so on circling round their edges, as we have in the chalk stream. In the slow stream trout may make more use of these glides than in the fast one, because the speed, though greater than before planting, will not be excessive. At least in the

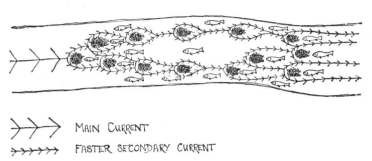

WEED PLANTING IN A
SLOW FEEDER STREAM

MAIN CURRENT
FASTER SECONDARY CURRENT

FIG 29   Weed planting in slow water

upstream section of the chalk-stream stretch, the divided currents will still be strong.

In both streams the fish may use the slack water bordered by the forked currents for resting in, but in the fast stream they will use these also for lying in during the feeding periods, when they will intercept food coming down on the current margins. In the slow stream their feeding positions will often be in the glides, for the speed of these can be ideal for the transport of duns and spinners, and the perfect feeding position for trout is where the surface-borne food can be taken with the least amount of body movement.

To establish our glides in slow streams we make use of whatever natural aids the stretch possesses, using as planting stations any bends, or pieces of bank that jut into the river, and always planting just downstream of these. In the fast chalk stream we either ignore these features, or plant just upstream of them, thus making the channel of water that finds its way round the obstruction. Wherever a natural impediment to the flow occurs, it will be a place where, immediately downstream, there will be some quickening of the flow, though it may be only slight. Our job is to turn a slight speed-up into a useful glide. We are working in terms of localised habitats, striving to make these acceptable to trout.

Reference to the sketch plans will show that in the chalk stream we have split a fast current into numerous divisions, with the object of attaining a lesser volume of fast water throughout the stretch. In overall terms we have probably not greatly lessened the speed of flow; in fact we may well have increased it among the split currents at the highest end of the stretch. But we have replaced the original 'bore' of fast water with narrow channels in association with slacker areas.

In the slow stream we have turned a slow 'bore' into faster channels, while still retaining a comparatively slow flow overall. Thus we have not changed the basic nature of the water, which is all to the good, for we are not trying to do that, and could not without embarking on engineering projects. We are in no way trying to establish artificial conditions; we are simply setting out to make the best possible use of existing ones.

In our slow stream *Ranunculus peltatus* and *R. aquatilis* would be good plants, and might be growing somewhere near at hand in the stream, or in local ditches, provided these had not all succumbed to the piping and filling-in mania. These, having floating leaves, would be the ones most likely to create barriers to the flow and thus turn it round the plant margins at an increased speed.

It is perhaps worth pointing out that where suitable plants are scarce in one's own locality they can be brought from elsewhere, provided they are wrapped in damp material. If they cannot be planted at once, they should be placed temporarily in the stream, suitably anchored to the bank.

We cannot expect newly planted beds to provide immediate improvements. They must first grow and become established, a process that will take about three seasons. My sketch plan shows the likely course of events at the end of this period. The trout symbols indicate the positions which would be most favoured, but they should not necessarily be taken to mean that fish would invariably be present in the numbers shown, taking the stretch as a hundred yards, though they could be without much difficulty.

It will be seen that the fast secondary currents in the chalk stream proceed for quite long distances, and therefore enclose relatively long areas of slacker water in which trout will lie. In the slow stream exactly the reverse applies. The planting has not split a slow main current into long secondary fast ones, but has split it into only very short glides, with correspondingly smaller areas of slack water.

Although the slow-water planting system has established trout lies, it has also made the fishing difficult, because the trout now have an abundance of weed to make for when they are on the hook. Other factors are less open water on which to cast, and a greater danger of being snagged on weed. Furthermore, the system would not be ideal for rainbow trout, which tend to move about instead of taking up more or less fixed feeding stations as brown trout in streams do.

However, the casting problems we must accept; they exist to be overcome and offer a fine challenge to the angler's skill. They call not only for precise aiming of the fly, but also for a high degree of expertise in playing the fish. Techniques will vary according to experience. In spite of Skues's dictum about a checked fish going to weed and an unchecked one floundering on the surface, which is true enough as a basic principle, there are times when the trout must be hustled, and 'skated' over the weed. My son gave me a remarkable demonstration of this on the Kennet, where a trout was feeding under the opposite bank, nearly thirty yards away, and separated from the casting bank by wide beds of weed. Had he attempted to play that fish in the accepted sense, he would almost certainly have been in dire trouble. As it was the fish was brought over the weed beds and into the net within thirty seconds.

Such shock tactics, in a modified form, may be called for in the planted section of slow stretches, though they are unlikely to be so drastic as in the example quoted, because the stream would be narrower, the line shorter, and the probability of maintaining control while allowing the fish some line would be greater. But it still remains for us to be prepared to adapt our methods to what may well be trying circumstances.

It is, of course, possible to compromise in slow water by using groins in some places instead of weeds, but weeds would still be necessary to oxygenate the water and to provide living quarters for nymphs etc. Where improvement by weed planting alone would create too many difficulties for the angler, then the obvious way round the problem would be to combine weed beds with groins.

The latter take two basic forms; one is the boulder dam made up of large stones or slabs, which may go right across a stream to create a waterfall and the resultant water disturbance for some yards below it; the other is the local obstruction jutting out obliquely from the bank in a 'downstream and across' position. The boulder dam may also be modified to suit this purpose.

The commonest form of groin is made of pairs of upright 'runners' firmly sunk in the stream bed, down which a stout plank is slid, of sufficient depth to allow its top edge to be high enough above the water to create a waterfall. The number of pairs of runners will depend on the length of the groin, and may be no more than two, that is one each end, if the groin is short, or three or four pairs if it is long.

If the groin is deep, then two, or possibly three planks, slid down edge to edge, will be needed. In fact, two planks as a minimum are better than one, since it is then possible to adjust according to rising or falling water levels.

The most effective place to insert a groin is just below necks and bends in the bank, or where there is a piece of bank jutting into the water, as such places always cause some speed up of the flow in their immediate vicinity, and so provide an initial advantage.

Physically, groins are superior to weed beds for speeding the flow, because their impact on the water is immediate, and is also more marked. Water falls over the top and curls round the edges. In the lee of the groin the conditions are very similar to those in the lee of a weed bed, but again are more quickly established and usually more evident. A pool is formed in the lee, of quiet water and of some depth, which makes a first-rate trout lie. The curling water round the edges likewise suits trout admirably, and traps spent spinners and newly emerged duns.

But whatever their undoubted virtues, groins cannot replace plants in the overall scheme, for the simple reason that although they are agents in the aerating of water, through the turbulence they cause, they are inert matter lacking the chemistry of plants.

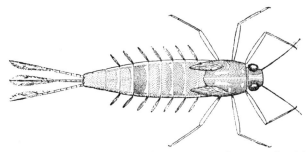

FIG 30   Nymph of Pale Evening Dun, *Procloëon pseudorufulum*, 8mm long, from life

They therefore contribute nothing to the life forces of the aquatic environment—save for the aerating effects they have on the water, and the algal communities they attract, and their presence alone will not bring about conditions to encourage surface-feeding trout. But where they are used in conjunction with a modified planting system, the value of both will be at its maximum and fewer plants will be needed.

A groin led off at an angle from one bank and terminated at a yard or so from the opposite bank will divert water into the latter, where it will delve out a good bankside pool. If the bank which receives the diverted water is soft and liable to erosion, it is wise to buttress it with deeply sunk corrugated iron at two or three feet behind the point of impact, with side pieces as appropriate, to prevent excessive wearing away, though often such a precaution is necessary only if the diverted flow is strong, and in many streams needing this kind of treatment the force is insufficient to cause bank erosion. But at all times one should avoid diverting the water into the root area of a bankside tree.

Silt will usually build up in some measure behind the groin, especially the board type, but it is a simple matter to release this during winter by removing the boards. Properly constructed boulder dams, which do not present a broad, wall-like obstruction on their upstream side but are sloped from the top, do not hold up silt to any serious extent, and any that does accumulate can be

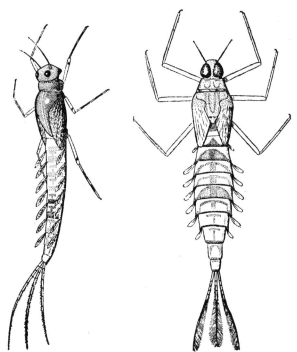

Fig 31   Nymph of Little Sky-Blue, syn Pale Watery,
Small Spurwing, *Centroptilum luteolum*,
7mm long, from life

Fig 32   Nymph of Blue-winged Pale Watery, syn Pale Watery,
Large Spurwing, *Centroptilum pennulatum*,
9mm long, from life

useful, since it fills in cracks and crannies in the dam and helps to bond the structure. The sloping surface also preserves the dam from a too concentrated weight of water, causing the flow to slide up over the top instead of percolating through the base and undermining it.

Here it might be mentioned that slow-flowing streams in which we are carrying out this kind of improvement can be very deceptive to the inexperienced eye. They look harmless enough, but we should remember the old saying about dripping water wearing away a stone. We do not have drips, but unless we build the dam correctly we have something far more insidious, which is the weight of moving water pressing against a surface broadside against the flow.

An encouraging result of good improvement in slow waters is that a nice balance is formed between a flow that was previously a little too slow for certain nymphs, and one that, after the improvement, is not too fast for these.

Thus we should find such species appearing as the Pale Evening Dun, *Procloëon pseudorufulum* (Fig 30), the Little Sky Blue, *Centroptilum luteolum* (Fig 31) and, with luck, the rare Blue-winged Pale Watery, *C. pennulatum* (Fig 32). These, together with the Olives, Iron Blues and so on that should also colonise the water, would constitute a trout larder of a type that almost certainly would not have been there before.

CHAPTER 13

Bankside Herbage

ALTHOUGH BANKSIDE plants are not part of the fly-fisher's flora as far as fly life is concerned, they are none the less a part of the fishing scene; their value does not stop at providing a screen into which flies may be blown for shelter in high winds. They serve an aesthetic and a practical purpose. The first is obvious, though it is sad to hear any number of anglers condemning waterside plants and demanding that they should be cut down to grass level on the grounds that they inhibit casting.

We have only to compare the walking surfaces along plantless stream edges with those along streams where plants flourish to recognise the bonding function which herbage fulfils. It is nature's buttress against bank erosion Where there is growth there will be a firm surface up to its edge (Plate 8, p 71); where there is no growth there will often be insidious penetration of the water, and a soggy, unstable margin, at least along streams associated with water meadows, or whose level rises perceptibly in winter or at flood times.

Another most useful function of bankside vegetation is to shelter fish and obscure the fishermen. From behind a good clump of willowherb, or meadowsweet, or hemp agrimony, an angler can stalk his fish, watch its movements, and get much closer than he can where there is nowhere to hide (Plate 10, p 72).

Excessive growth must obviously be trimmed, and there is frequently a case for cutting out gaps in long, unbroken stretches of tall vegetation. But the amount to be trimmed or removed should be no more than is necessary to provide reasonable casting conditions. The trouble is that what is reasonable to a skilled caster is utterly unreasonable to an unskilled one. So it really comes down to improving our casting; we want to rise to the demands, not fall to the level of incompetence.

Every skilled fly fisher delights in bank herbage; its very presence keeps him on his toes, metaphorically if not actually, and he adjusts his timing, his distance, and his casting, to overcome the undoubted hazards to his fly. It is a matter not of making things more difficult than they need be, but of accepting existing difficulties, knowing that they are inherent in a waterside scene that offers the highest degree of interest and variation. A stream without its many-scented and many-coloured marginal plants can be distinctly featureless, and it is probably the shorn banks one too often sees that have given rise to the ultimate angling blasphemy, namely that chalk streams are dull.

Bankside plants do not in any event grow along the entire bank. There are many lengths devoid of them, but if beginners imagine these are easy places, then they soon learn better. Concealment is almost impossible, save by lying prone on one's stomach, a position not calculated to make for precision casting. The only approach is from considerably downstream of one's fish, which means a long cast and a greater possibility of losing the fish if it does take the fly. It is, of course, possible to creep fairly close, but it is surprising how the tension builds up, and tension is the last thing with which an inexperienced fly fisher should be assailed. The old hand feels it also, but in a different way. His philosophy, born of long years of fishing, enables him to cope with the situation with far greater equanimity. For one thing he can judge the length of his throw to a nicety—to an inch or so, if not a millimetre—while the tyro will, in his pent-up state, almost certainly overshoot, or else undershoot, when he will have to make another cast, assuming the fish to still be there. If he overshoots, the trout will probably take fright and dart off.

But behind a great clump of willowherb there is a feeling of security. True, the chances of muffing the throw are just as great, but at least the tension is lower, and as we contemplate the quarry we have a nice comfortable feeling that he is completely unaware of our presence, whereas with the trout in unfringed water we can never feel really sure.

It must however be admitted that waterside plants can play havoc with flies that are inexpertly cast, and since the learner finds this out very early in his fishing career, it is possible that bankside growths, far from giving him a sense of security, will in no time at all become regarded as the most infuriating objects on the face of the earth. Thus does he come to hate them and to demand their destruction.

Let us not wreak revengeful blows upon these innocent and beautiful things. If they clutch at our flies, it is because we have directed the flies into their clutches. They have not reached out and grabbed a perfectly delivered Iron Blue; it is we who have imperfectly delivered that missile and caused it to land among the leaves and blossoms.

That blasphemous charge of dullness cannot be sustained where there are kingcups in spring and many flowering plants in summer. These make a trout stream, as far as its visual aspects are concerned, but apart from that they are as vital a part of the bank environment as the water plants are of the aquatic. The two are linked indivisibly; each complements the others, and no stream is complete without its natural fringe.

Conclusion

HAVING NOW come to the end of this brief study, I am all too conscious of its many inadequacies and sins of omission. I can only trust there are not too many sins of commission.

Omissions and inadequacies in a book that seeks to concentrate mainly on one aspect of fly fishing are inevitable, because the innumerable factors that make up the subject of fly fishing in its entirety are so closely interwoven that it becomes extremely difficult to divorce any single one from a number of others without leaving many gaps in the story.

On the other hand, to deal with the subject from A to Z would need a volume so immense that it would need some kind of lifting apparatus to get it on to the table, or else a series of volumes for which nobody would have the shelf space.

So I have tried to find some middle way, and when I launched myself on the project one of my principal aims was to try to show that there is a great deal more to fly fishing than just catching fish.

I firmly believe that to get the best out of the sport, and to derive from it the greatest interest, we should have at least a working knowledge of the trout's environment. From that knowledge there stems a much deeper appreciation of the value of the plants. We no longer see them with half an eye, merely taking them for granted as so much water weed; we no longer either accept them vaguely as serving some purpose which is no doubt useful but which we cannot precisely define, or as watery jungles that seem to fulfil little function other than snagging up our flies.

If this book inspires an interest in the plants of trout waters, where there was no interest before, or if it increases a previously faint concern with these plants, it will have proved worth the writing, and I shall go to the streamside a happy man.

Index